NATURE REALMS ACROSS AMERICA

NATURE REALMS ACROSS AMERICA

JOSEPH JAMES SHOMON

THE AMERICAN FORESTRY ASSOCIATION

PREFACE

We are often reminded nowadays that the Earth is no longer a revolving sphere of rock, water, gas and living protoplasm. More realistically it is a world of many other worlds, many systems, each delicately interwoven with the next and all strangely interlocked with one another. In one sense, our living planet is a collection of living communities, ranging from the smallest of plant and animal worlds to the largest. Indeed, any unit capable of carrying on life by combining hydrogen, carbon, oxygen and sunlight is a kind of manufacturing plant —a plant which ecologists call an ecosystem. Thus a pool of swamp water—even a molecule of sea water if it receives light—is capable of functioning as a complete living unit.

In North America a number of large ecosystems can be identified —seashore, deciduous forest, grassland, coniferous forest, alpine, and tundra. Unfortunately, there is no universal agreement on the extent and number of these kingdoms, or their exact boundaries.

Some view our whole land continent as a single ecosystem; others include entire oceans and seas. In some ways the entire earth, its land mass, its seas, its thin film of hydrogen and oxygen wrapped around it, can be pictured as one large living community, the biosphere.

This viewing of our world through the eyes of the ecologist makes good sense. Moreover, many students of nature sooner or later reach the conclusion that such thinking is the only realistic way in which to view our environment. Unfortunately, the ecological viewpoint is a slow-awakening process and to most people, comes too late in life. The problem nowadays is to gain an early ecological understanding of nature, for only through such understanding and viewpoint can the future have much meaning for us.

JOSEPH JAMES SHOMON

CONTENTS

ILLUSTRATIONS

All black and white photographs by JOSEPH J. SHOMON, *except where otherwise noted.*

The bristlecone pine, oldest living thing on earth, makes its last stand in the high alpine country, as here in California's White Mountains. (p. 185)

Glacier Peak Wilderness, Washington. *Photo by Ernie Rosenau* (p. 187)

High Alpine lands are found on western mountain peaks and in much of the Rocky Mountain area. (p. 190)

The great Hudsonian coniferous forest, reaching down from Canada into our western mountains, is dominated by spruce and fir. (p. 200)

Picturesque, wild, and still largely unspoiled, the Hudsonian forest is America's last true wilderness. (p. 210)

A lone white spruce attests to the onslaught of the Arctic tundra winds. (p. 216)

The Arctic tundra northwest of Churchill, Manitoba is a biome as untouched as any on earth. (p. 221)

A musk ox herd goes into a defense ring on Bathurst Island in the Canadian Arctic Archipelago. (p. 233)

Stampeding barrenground caribou on the Arctic prairies. (p. 236)

Continental Divide, Glacier National Park, Montana. *Photo by David Muench.*
(Front of Jacket)

Drawings by Wayne Trimm, P. Wright and Ned Smith.

FOREWORD

There are sound reasons, scientific, economic, esthetic, and ethical for what we loosely call "conservation." But no matter how convincing these may be or how cleverly they may be implemented by laws and techniques, they have little chance to be effective unless we learn to cherish the environment of which we are an inseparable part. For if experience teaches us anything, it is that people will take care only of what they appreciate, be these gardens, animals, books, homes, fine art, machines, or other human beings.

I know no formula that explains why people value the things they do. Anyone who has watched children grow up knows how varied and seemingly accidental such choices seem to be. Certainly some choices, especially those which are extraordinarily intense, have their basis in heredity. But most of us owe our tastes and interests largely to the influence of others who are already knowledgeable and enthusiastic.

And now, just at this critical time in our nation's history when so much depends on whether we learn to cherish our vast and varied environment, along comes Joseph Shomon to share with us his rich experience among living communities scattered from arctic to tropics, from marsh to desert.

His enthusiasm, expressed in his own words rather than the stilted language of the pedant, is infectious. So well has he described what he has seen and done that readers, whether lay or professional, will find their interest sustained, their intelligence respected, and their vision enlarged.

PAUL B. SEARS

NATURE REALMS ACROSS AMERICA

THE MARVELOUS RAIN FOREST

THE RAIN FOREST IS A STRANGELY MARVELOUS PLACE. IT IS STRANGE because to so many it is an unfamiliar world, a forest of mystery, even foreboding. Yet to those who would choose adventure and seek to know this land as it should be known, it is a remarkable world of nature.

Over the millions of years that the rain forest has evolved to its present state it has been a region of great happenings, of much growth, sudden death, and constant resurrection. And to modern man in recent times it has become a very special wilderness—a wilderness known only to a relatively small number—but one of enormous spiritual refreshment and deep meaning.

A visible thread, universal as life, binds all rain forests together —water. Abundant and certain, this special resource in the rain forest is like sunlight to the desert. Were it not for at least four inches of rainfall each month and some 120 inches a year, the rain forest would not survive—at least not as a true rain forest. This water, this basic aqueous substance of all life, comes in varied forms. It creeps into the rain forest as mist and fog. It steals over the green wilderness mantle as moisture laden clouds, rising and billowing and balling together to release all sorts of rains. The rains come in drizzle or a gentle shower or heavy rain. Often it comes as a thunderstorm or a turbulent downpour. At times, in some places, it comes as a drenching, devastating hurricane, or as a destructive monsoon.

There are American rain forests that grow luxuriant vegetation on 150 inches of rain a year. Others do beautifully on 100. The tropical rain forests of Africa and Asia are almost continually soaked in rainfall. The huge Amazon basin wilderness wreathes under more than 400 inches of rainfall annually. Only one small area in the world receives more rain, this is Mt. Waialeale in Hawaii. Here a 5,170 foot volcanic peak regularly receives over 450 inches of rain annually. One year the area established the world's record for wetness—a grand total of 471.68 inches of rainfall.

Displayed in the rain forest is also the universal oneness of year-round greenery—foliage that always looks a shade of avocado green. And nearly everywhere except in temperate climes this forest reveals trees with broad leaves. But major differences do occur in the various rain forests.

Cradled between a crest of mountain ranges in northwest Washington and the frothing Pacific sea lies the unique rain forest of the Olympics—one of the unspoiled wonderlands of America and the only true *coniferous* rain forest in the world. Unlike the wet forests of Central America and the Amazon River Basin, this forest is clothed with needle-bearing trees and to the sojourner feels refreshingly cool. In the wet tropics the vegetation is dull green, at times even brownish, and the air is uncomfortably warm and moist, very much like being in a green house conservatory. It is damp in the Olympics too but it is a humidity that one can bear comfortably. When it is not raining, the coolish temperature and moist conditions pass unnoticed.

The first time I saw this forest I was strongly reminded of several other lush temperate forests I had seen: the McMillan Forest on Vancouver Island in British Columbia and the high Fraser fir forests of the Great Smokies. Both have an annual rainfall in the sixties and both are majestic. In the green mansion-like valleys of the Olympics, especially along the slopes of the Queets and the Hon, a combination of natural conditions harmoniously combine to create a superb wet wilderness—a marvelous world of 160 inches of rainfall a year. The rain does not pour out of the skies for long torrential weeks, as in the Amazon, but rather it comes more frequently as easy and steady soaking rain. There is also a big difference between this forest and the tropical type in the number and length of sun-lit days—the latter having quite a number, the Olympics having relatively few.

Although the vegetation is dense in both rain forests, the Olympics have a plant life that is strikingly different from that of the humid forests of the equatorial zone. I recall one grove along the Hoh where four big evergreen species make up the bulk of the forest growth— Douglas-fir, Sitka spruce, western hemlock, and western redcedar. And these beautiful conifers are seemingly always in association with western red alder, a hardwood or broad-leaved tree.

The virgin Olympic rain forest, like its tropical counterpart, has an understory zone that makes for easy walking. It is not dense. Denseness comes when natural conditions occur to provide openings in the thick canopy or when lumbering takes place and more sunlight reaches the ground and promotes heavy growth.

To stroll along a fern-lined trail in the Olympic water-dripping wilderness or to sit on a huge moss covered log (almost always it's a nurse log) is to savor the mood and spirit of a noble wilderness. The sounds are memorable: birds sing, squirrels chatter, trees squeak in the wind. Occasionally, if one is lucky, he can in the fall of the year hear the distant bugle of an Olympic elk. Or rarer still, he may catch the far-off tomcat snarl of a wandering mountain lion.

One winter day I returned to the Olympics after a long absence. They had not changed. I sat musing in a grove of Douglas-fir giants studying a large nurse log. I took out my penknife and cut into a green blanket of moss which covered the log. It was five inches thick. The prostrate monarch obviously had lain here for many years. Along the log grew at least a dozen sizable red alder trees and one large fir. I took out my increment borer and walked over to the Douglas-fir and drilled it. The central core sample showed many annual rings and I counted them. The young fir was forty years old. How much longer the fallen log had lain there before the fir seedling sprouted is anyone's guess, maybe two, maybe twenty years. The point is that here was a fallen giant which in death had given rise to a whole row of new trees and countless other plants. Here were mosses of several kinds, lichens and liverworts, ferns, fungi. Here too were a host of smaller plants I could not identify.

When I told this to my colleagues, Dick Bower and Tom Stewart, long-time natives of the Pacific Northwest, they thought I was low in my estimate of the years that the fallen giant had lain in this wilderness. "Some of these big mossback logs have been here in the virgin rain forest a hundred years," Dick said. "And when they finally pass on into the soil, they anchor with them many supporting trees. Some of course die away. Others live. This often accounts for the long straight rows of trees one sees in the Olympic virgin rain forest."

The true rain forest regardless of origin or place exudes a serenity and peace that is all its own. The peace, in essence, is of a wild and wilderness quality and it permeates deep into one's being. Even our restricted rain forest of the West coast does this, but the spirit is more pronounced in the wild, extensive rain forests of the tropics, like those of Panama, Columbia, Ecuador, Venezuela, Peru and Brazil. There the feeling is overpowering. The quality seems so strong as to cast a questioning note on the term *rain forest* itself. Perhaps these forests in their truest sense or personality should be called *rain wilderness*.

It is unfortunate that the tropical rain forest has been vicariously depicted as a terribly fearsome, even sinister place, filled with biting insects and poisonous snakes and visibly portraying great life-death struggles in a seemingly thick and hostile environment. While some conditions like this do exist, and on a minor scale, the true rain forest on the contrary is a delightful and enchanting place. Certainly it is not anything like what some stories and films would have us believe.

Because most rain forests occur along the equatorial belt, in broad bands up to 10 to 12 degrees north and south of the equator and are much misunderstood, it seems proper that more attention should be given this biotic kingdom.

World-wide the tropical rain forest is largely an equatorial plant kingdom. In Africa rain forests occur in Ghana, Gold Coast, Sierra Leone, and the Congo. In Asia they cover parts of India, Ceylon, Indo-China, Malaysia, Australia, Philippines, New Zealand, and parts of Hawaii. In Central America one can find rain forests in parts of Mexico, Costa Rica, Honduras, El Salvador, Guatemala, and Panama. In the Greater and Lesser Antilles rain forests are found in Cuba, Jamaica, Puerto Rico, Martinique, Tobago, and Trinidad. In South America, Venezuela, Colombia, Ecuador, and Peru have the most extensive rain forests. The finest primary wet wilderness lies in the great Amazon basin.

What is the tropical rain wilderness really like? And what are the conditions like during daylight hours and at night? The answers choose a sea-level island in Panama, for example, and the month is depend on where one is and what time of the year he is there. If you December, then the chances are good you'll find the forest dripping wet. This is still the rainy season and downpours are frequent. The thoughtful visitor simply dresses lightly and prepares to get wet. And this need not be all bad, for even in the rain there is much to see that is refreshing and fascinating.

If the object of your visit is Barro Colorado Island (which in Spanish means Red Mud Island), you will have the convenience of walking on well-established trails. A morning's hike or an afternoon's jaunt over this 4,000-acre rain forest can be the experience of a lifetime. One quickly gets a true feeling for the tropical wilderness, its terrain, its innumerable plants and animals, not to mention the awe and spirit of the landscape. The mood, however, is always one of wetness. Even when the weather is clear, as happens for short periods, the trails are soggy, quite dark, and at times almost gloomy. The tree cover is so heavy and so thick that sunlight rarely filters down to the ground, and one must sort of prowl around downstairs in semi-darkness. But as soon as one loses his fear of lurking snakes and encounters with other strange animals (such encounters are rare), the strolling becomes interesting if not joyous.

One of the impressive features about this tropical wilderness is its luxuriant growth—trees towering 100 to 150 feet into the bright sky, vines dropping down on all sides, and many spindly immature trees trying to push their way into the tightly closed canopy. The vines are of many woody types, some as much as a foot wide, many straight, others twisted and coiled like serpents. This forest is known to have over 200 species of woody vines alone and over 1400 species of higher plants. The trees and liana vines are all broad-leaved and usually thin-barked. Palms of various types grow where the vegetation is less dense.

Some trails curve up and down over rough terrain, but many are easily negotiated along ridges. Where the grades are severe, walking becomes a bit uneasy. The ground often is wet, almost mucilaginous, and slipping and sliding are frequent. There is little ground litter as the fallen wet leaves decay rapidly due to the excessive heat and moisture. All types of roots cross the trails, some wormlike, some feathery, a few strangely twisted and coiled resembling the deadly fer-de-lance. I ran across one such sinister form in a trail the first afternoon, halted and studied it a long time. Then I finally realized that it was a root.

The big trees have telephonepole-like trunks and are often straight and limbless for 50 or more feet. They are thin-barked like our North American eastern beeches and in most cases are extremely buttresssed at the ground. A tree with a bole only four feet in diameter for 60 feet may spread out at the base by more than twenty times its main trunk size. The swells rise up 8 to 15 feet before they taper off. The buttressed bases take many shapes, some spider-like with huge arms for roots, others fluted and ridged, still others flattened vertically and board-like in appearance. No one really knows just why tropical trees buttress this way. It may be a support adaptation in the shallow soils or nature's way of getting the trees out of standing water. The latter reason seems mystifying here because many of the buttressed trees are found on steep ridges far from standing water. But small pools of water are often seen on ridges where the buttresses form into boat-like basins holding water as much as a foot deep for days.

Occasionally one sees trees that are heavily prop-rooted, like a cornstalk with its roots very much out of the soil. Botanists believe that these trees first develop on soil mounds, and that as the soil washes away, the prop roots are left exposed. Here and there one notices mounds of mud in the trees, like huge wasps' nests. These are termite houses. They are built 8 to 15 feet above ground to keep them out of the water. Each nest is connected to the soil by a series of mud tubes along the tree trunk. Several species of anteaters enjoy taking positions next to these tubes and nests, lapping up the busy termites which frantically try to repair the holes that the anteater makes.

Animal life is not visibly abundant during the daylight hours in the Panamanian rain forest. Now and then the stealthy sojourner will see a reddish squirrel or perhaps the larger rodent, agouti. This small mammal, technically called *Dasyprocta agouti,* is preyed upon extensively by wild cats and snakes. The genus is composed of about two dozen species which range from southern Mexico through Central America to southern Brazil and to the Lesser Antilles. The animals are found in cool, damp, lowland forests, grassy streambanks, thick brush, high, dry hillsides, savannahs and cultivated areas. They have a small pig-like body with a rabbit-like head, and burrow under boulders, tree roots and into river banks. Their chief food consists of fruits, vegetables and succulent plants. Agoutis bear two litters a year, with two to four young in a litter, born in a burrow. Hunted for their excellent flesh, these interesting rodents are dwindling in numbers.

Occasionally your scanning eyes may spot a two-toed or three-toed sloth half-way up some tree, hanging upside down by his large hooked claws. The sloth is a slow, dull-witted creature that feeds on leaves and wishes no harm to anyone. On rare occasions a lucky visitor may spot a tapir, a curved-nosed gentle relative of the rhinoceros, as he moves slowly through the green underbrush. The wild pig, or peccary, is more commonly seen, usually in small groups.

Along shorelines and in swampy places, the large capybara—the world's largest rodent—can sometimes be spotted. This animal has a large, blunt snout, no tail, and enjoys playing with floating coconuts and other large fruits which drop into its watery domain. The capybara or *Hydrochoerus hydrochoerus* is also called water hog. Only one genus and two species are known. It inhabits woods and dense vegetation around lakes, ponds, rivers, streams, marshes and swamps. When fully grown, a male may reach four feet and weigh 120 lbs.; females are smaller. They live in bands or family groups up to 20 individuals. These big rodents are semiaquatic in nature, feeding on grasses and aquatic plants. Adept in water, these animals are able to swim under water for considerable distances. The female bears a single litter of two to eight young per year. The life span of the species is eight to ten years.

A close relative of the agouti and capybara is the paca, a rodent with spotted brownish fur and hoof-like toes. In addition, seven different rats are present and three different mice. Also found in Panama are six different opossums, 28 bats, two anteaters, two sloths, two peccaries, two deer, and a single species of raccoon, coati, kinkajou, olingo, tayra, otter, puma, jaguar, ocelot, yaguarundi, and tapir to make up a total of 74 mammal species.

By far the most commonly seen mammals in the tropical wet wilderness are the monkeys. Five species occur on Barro Colorado Island alone—the black mantled howler monkey, night monkey, spider monkey, marmoset, and the capuchin. The howler is not easily seen but of course is heard a great deal. The marmoset is one of the smallest of monkeys with thick, soft and brightly colored fur. The capuchin is also a small monkey but with a whitish face and a hoodlike crown of black hair.

The howler almost never comes down out of the trees; the spiders are more readily seen, usually climbing lianas or swinging from limb to limb or tree to tree. They are long-armed and one sees much feet and tail when they move about. The tail of this agile monkey is so prehensile that they can thrust it out and draw a branch or fruit to to its body. Unlike the howler the spider makes little noise.

The howler monkeys are the real noisemakers in the rain forest. Over a long period of evolutionary time the howler has developed a hollow-boned voice box behind the base of his tongue which enables him to give a roaring, deafening sound when an intruder (man or beast) approaches. The bark is strange, loud, and at times terrifying. The roar of a whole troop of howlers has been described as one of the most awful, fearful sounds in the animal world. When angered a big male howler can be heard up to two miles away and a troop perhaps up to three or four. Howling occurs mostly at dawn and in the evening, although it can begin any time.

One late afternoon on Barro Colorado I was walking a trail in the island's deep interior. It was getting dark and I was hurrying for the Smithsonian tropical research laboratory more than two miles away. Suddenly high in a tree top I saw a branch move. Freezing in my tracks, I studied the place where the disturbance took place. Then another branch snapped. Finally I was barely able to make out a dark object in the tree canopy. Then a weak chirp came out of the tree. Thinking it might be a black-mantled howler, I let out a series of low imitating calls. No answer came. Again, I let out a *huh . . . huuh . . . huh . . . hoo!* Then a soft *hur . . . hur* came back. I responded, louder and more defiant, this time. Apparently this was more than any howler could stand and one answered back sharply. Each time I called, he came back more strongly. Soon other howlers joined in. A chill raced down my spine, but I kept calling. In a few minutes a whole troop of howlers had become aroused, including one terribly loud, guttural male who was trying to scare the daylight out of me. We kept it up for fifteen or twenty bluffing minutes when I decided to call it off and let those interesting creatures be. The monkeys never came down out of the trees to feign an attack as some observers have reported; they were merely content to remain in their territorial upper forest garden.

There are other daytime sounds in the tropical rain forest to be sure—jungle rats, barking deer, and birds, mostly jungle parrots, toucans, macaws and woodpeckers. These birds are colorful but because the cover is so overwhelmingly green they are not easily visible in the heavy green forest.

Nor are the bright flowers particularly evident. Red and yellow bromeliads and other air plants occur in great profusion but, again, since the colors occur mostly in the lush forest canopy, the ground-walking visitor seldom sees them.

Rain forest sounds are most noticeable at night when the nocturnal creatures become active. In the Peruvian Amazon low country these sounds range from the splashing of caymans and turtles to the calls of the jungle turkey, doves, parrots, and small jungle deer. Deeper in this tropical wilderness the human ear may occasionally pick up the fierce snarl of a hunting jaguar or the soft hiss of the stealthy ocelot. Where howler monkeys are common, their calling is particularly pronounced.

In general, however, I have found the Amazon jungle to be nowhere as vocal or riotous as most people would believe. On one two and a half hour hunting trek through the Amazon wilderness in north-eastern Peru my tape recorder picked up only a few night sounds. Yet such a trek can be a nerve-taxing experience. The danger comes, of course, from lurking poisonous vipers, the fer-de-lance and the bush-master, both of which are active at night. The fer-de-lance is a big snake, up to 10 feet long, and can be aggressive when encountered. The bushmaster is more sluggish but more dangerous because of its size (up to 12 feet) and its very long fangs. It is considered to be the largest, most venomous viper in the world. It is said to have an incredibly long strike—five feet!

I did not run into any of these deadly vipers in Central or South America, although I did run across many reports of their presence. Actually I've seen more poisonous snakes in Virginia than in all my sojourns in the tropics.

The same can be said of troublesome insects. While mosquitoes and flies abound in the tropics—and more insect species occur there than in any other environment—I was not bothered by them too much. I have been eaten up more by mosquitoes in North Carolina and on the Arctic tundra than anywhere else in the New World.

Altogether five distinct types of tropical rain wilderness occur around the equator. The coastal rain forest is a low-lying ever-green forest found close to sea level, in low-land basins, and along streams

and rivers where the elevation is less than 500 feet. Much of the huge Amazon basin lies in this wilderness. It is marked by hot temperatures, very high humidity and an enormous amount of rainfall—as much as 400 inches a year in some places. Although explored in many areas, it is still a wild and haunting place. It is this virgin or true tropical wet wilderness that is the most primitive wilderness in the world.

Rain forests, as well as tropical forests in general, have been deteriorating as natural environments. Today there is much concern over what is happening to the original tropical forests that remain as well as those areas damaged by centuries of pillage and nomadic agriculture. The principal causes of despoliation of tropical forests, according to such experienced tropical foresters as Tom Gill and Frank Wadsworth, are two: the ruinous clearing of forest lands for agriculture and destructive logging. The former often is done on submarginal lands with poor soils resulting in frequent misuse, the lands then taking over by a riotous growth of worthless jungle growth which is almost impossible to manage or regenerate with useful species. The latter, destructive logging, is another serious deteriorating factor. In the Latin American tropical forests the two most sought after species are mahogany and Spanish cedar. As these species are cut out, usually along water courses by crude logging practices, great destruction follows. As Tom Gill says, ". . . three-fourths of the potentially productive forest areas in the American tropics suffer from poor or destructive cutting."

Much of today's tropical forest plight is due to the lack of knowledge of tropical forests. We have only meager information on the extent and character of tropical forests, on the great number of species present, their value or how to treat them. The remoteness and vastness and the difficulty of access are other factors. Moreover, the backwardness of many countries, their unstable governments and other risks make foreign capital investment slow. So research seems the key to the better and safer utilization of tropical forests. While the United States, Canada, and Great Britain are beginning to carry out more research in the tropics, the job ahead is enormous. The battle to safeguard tropical forests, as Mr. Gill points out, is joined, but "how many battles must be lost before the war on waste and destruction is won?"

Much of the Amazon rain wilderness has been disturbed by saw and ax and is splotched with second growth jungle, perhaps the most impenetrable forest of all. Here the thick, heavy undergrowth has come in, resulting in a profusion of green cover. Such forests occur mainly along rivers and streams where logging is easiest. Although only certain trees are removed, enough disturbance is made to create an impenetrable mixed forest condition.

Where man caused disturbances are unknown in the riverbottom country, for example, along the Amazon and the Orinoco and their tributaries, plant growth is exceedingly rapid. Only now are we beginning to discover just how rich these riverbottom lands really are. Flooded many times each year, the wet tropical wilderness is replenished with fertile sediment and silt, the fertile "mud soup" from millions of acres of uplands. After every major rain the floodland bottoms rise, spread over thousands of square miles, then recede only to leave a marked "silt line" across the once-flooded landscape. All plants—trees, shrubs, vines, perennials, and annuals respond to this periodic feeding and respond with riotous growth. Plants sprout quickly, mature fast, and die and decay just as rapidly. Very old, overmature trees and snags, contrary to general belief, are practically nonexistent in the tropical rain forest.

One thing is very clear to scientists today, that is that we know practically nothing about the complex ecology of tropical forests. Much needs to be learned before ways and means can be developed to properly manage and safeguard these forests.

At higher elevations in the tropics the rain forest takes on a storied character. At each 500 foot interval a different kind of forest growth predominates. At still higher elevations one begins to see the submontane forest—a rain forest found from 1200 feet to 4500 feet above sea level. Finally, above this forest spreads the ever-green montane region. This cool, wet wilderness is often shrouded in fog and clouds (hence the term *cloud forests*). The mid-slopes of the Andes facing the Amazon basin and the Pacific coast region in South America contain large sections of this type of tropical wilderness.

One of the best places to see the various tropical forest types is along a relatively short span of mountains in Venezuela, across the coast range facing the Caribbean Sea. At one point, at a place called Caribea, near Caracas, the visitor can take a modern sky lift from almost near sea level to the top of a cloud-covered mountain where the elevation is some 7,000 feet above sea level. This so-called *eco-climb* is an ecologist's dream, for in a space of 30 minutes he can go through four different tropical life zones and look down upon each at close range.

What one sees in the tropical rain forest depends on his powers of observation and method of study. In haste one sees little and tends to make superficial and often inaccurate judgments. Naturalists who take time to observe life in the wet tropics will find that most areas teem with living things. William Beebe, the well-known oceanographic and tropical naturalist, once studied a single tree for an entire week in the Amazon bush. He discovered an incredible number of animal forms in the tree itself, mostly birds which totalled over 75 species. But he also witnessed a vast aggregation of lesser animals on the ground. His last act was to gather up four square feet of duff and soil from beneath the tree, to be later analyzed aboard the ship that was taking him homeward. For days Beebe studied his loot, small sections of litter bit by bit. He reported having discovered all kinds of living organisms —ants, mites, insects, worms and parts of once living animal forms. He finally accounted for some 500 species of life which he could positively identify. He estimated that there were easily five hundred more organisms present but which either escaped his eye or which he could not identify—in other words, a thousand or more organisms in one four-foot-square section of Brazilian jungle. Indeed, the rain forest is a marvelous place.

THE SEA ISLAND WORLD

JUTTING HEADLANDS CUT OFF BY THE MOTHER SEA. SANCTUARIES OF rock, large and small, usurped by seals, sea otters, and wheeling birds. The delicate fragrance of blooming arbutus trees on shorebanks of black volcanic basalt. Granite hills, carpeted by spruce and white birch, yet isolated by whitecapped waters from the mainland coast. Low barriers of sand and silt lying mercilessly exposed to the winds and the pounding surf. Outcroppings of coral with turquoise-colored lagoons filled with incredible life forms, all struggling for survival. These and many other scenes bring to the mind's eye the strange and fascinating world of sea islands.

Part of the fascination of islands at sea stems from their wildness, part from their aloneness, for sea islands are special places. They are portions of a land surface ruled by the elements, the sun and the wind and the sea.

Sea islands suggest a kind of delightful uneasiness. Even when you are on a familiar island or within sight of land, you sense a certain amount of uncertainty. You step ashore, lightly and quickly, look around to get your bearings. But an hour or a day or a week on an island and the feeling vanishes. If you're a short-time visitor, the chances are good you wished you had planned a longer stay. If you're a resident islander, you may sigh in relief and vow never to go to the mainland again.

Sea islands come in countless numbers and in many forms. Large islands along our continental rim run into the hundreds; small islands number into the thousands; islets of sea-splashed rock or sand can be counted in the millions. And each island, large or small, flat or mountainous, has one thing in common; it is a segregated chunk of the earth's exposed land surface surrounded by the sea. But the apartness of an island is never complete, for all islands in one way or another are tied to some continental land mass. They are never fully detached places. Bermuda is on an atoll 600 miles out in the Atlantic, yet when you are there you sense a strong linkage to coastal Georgia and South Carolina. Trinidad lies a scanty fifty miles from Venezuela, and is tethered to the River Orinoco, much as Vancouver Island is tied to the mainland of British Columbia. If a common thread joins islands together and islands to the land, it is the profound ingredient that ties all natural kingdoms together—the wondrous persistence and stability of life itself.

The life on sea islands is a parade of familiar and unfamiliar inhabitants. Visibly they walk or crawl or creep over mud or sand or rock; or they fly over the surfaces of large or small land areas; or they swim precariously in different marine habitats. Invisibly some life forms steal into wet and dry crevices or remain exposed to the elements. Life is often harsh on an island and it is easy to see why some living things don't make it.

And the smaller the island the more difficult the task of plant and animal survival. On the larger islands where the climate is favorable plants and animals tend toward a more complex interrelationship, seemingly almost to promote their own survival. Species are also more numerous. On a bare rock off the coast of Newfoundland or on a coral islet in the Bahamas, life becomes established only after great difficulty. But somehow, in some mysterious way, life gets started and survives.

I once came upon a bare rock on City Island in Long Island Sound.

No one could explain how this rock came to be where it was. One day it just appeared there in the water not far from shore. Perhaps a violent storm rolled over this glacial erratic and exposed its bare ten-foot surface to the chopping waves. At any rate, when I first saw the rock it was completely bare and as smooth as polished wet marble. I returned many times to my rock while flounder fishing and each spring and fall noticed that it took on more and more life. Today, nearly four decades later, the rock is completely encrusted with barnacles, small oysters, mussels, sea lettuce, blue algae, and rockweed. Life forms have colonized this rock against great odds. There was the record as plain as any textbook.

No one knows how many sea islands belong to the North American continent. No person has taken the trouble to count them. A conservative guess would be that they easily number a million. Alaska has more than 500 large islands and the Bahamas, although not true off-shore islands but Caribbean sea keys, has 700.

Three basic types of sea islands fringe the North American continent: Those islands which consist largely of rock and are akin to the rocks of the main coast; islands of sand or sand and silt and mud which lie very close to the mainland; the islands of coral rock where the sea waters are tropical. Like the individual beads of a necklace, each island can be much like its next door neighbor, or it can be strangely different. In my lifetime I have lived on, vacationed at, or visited over a hundred different islands and found no two exactly alike. The one central characteristic that lends charm to sea islands and gives them special beauty is diversity. Very often it is this trait that leads an island to its own downfall or destruction. By their great popularity with humans sea islands can become desecrated and even end up as island slums. Such situations have occurred where there is no planning and little nature appreciation.

Rocky Ramparts

Rocky sea islands are among the most diversified of land forms and nowhere in North America is a coastline so studded with different kinds of islands as in the Pacific Northwest. Here from northern California to the outermost reaches of the Aleutians one can see a garland of picturesque islands which rate as second to none in the world. It is the dream country of outdoorsmen and travellers. Whether you're a hunter, fisherman, photographer, artist, or naturalist, this region is a realm of nature to behold. So overpowering is its scenery and so awe-inspiring its natural beauty that more pictures have been taken of it and more said and written about it than any other landscape in the northern hemisphere.

My first introduction to the sea islands of the Pacific Northwest came after World War II when I was travelling on the continent in connection with a doctoral research mission. My studies in environmental conservation took me to all of the States as well as to the Provinces of Canada. In my itinerary was a series of visits to the coastal islands of British Columbia and Alaska. My landing on some of them was only long enough for me to want to return, again and again, which I did.

An island which proved to be enormously interesting was Lesquite. It is a handsome rugged island of perhaps a thousand acres and located in the middle of the straits of Georgia, east of big Vancouver Island. What makes this island special, I believe, is its isolation and naturalness. Only a few Canadian families live on it, sharing their life with its fantastic forest growth and wildlife.

Here on a bright warm August day, while fishing for salmon along its shores one can see the bald eagle soaring over the tops of big Douglas-fir trees, and perhaps spot the stick nest of an eagle pair. You can see seals basking on the rocks, sea birds working over schools of fish, and on rare occasions, killer whales wallowing in the straits. You can go ashore at low tide and dig butter clams to your heart's content or pick choice oysters from enormous beds between the cliffs. Ashore, you can romp with wild goats on the island's untrammelled interior and on rugged hillside openings pick Himalayan blackberries so huge they look like plums.

Near Lesquite is another island, Taxada. It is a larger sea island particularly noted for its reddish barked arbutus or madrone trees

which literally perfume the whole island for weeks in May and June. It too is wild and almost completely uninhabited. Douglas-fir, western hemlock, western redcedar and red alder are its principal trees, making a dense forest cover for the whole island. Near the wetter coastal bluffs, the ground cover beneath the trees is so thick with sword fern, shrubs, and vines that walking through is impossible. In one way the vegetation is very much like that of Vancouver Island as well as the mainland of British Columbia.

A somewhat different, small, island is Hornby. My Seattle eye surgeon friend, C. Thomas Stewart, who spends his vacations on Vancouver Island, largely salmon fishing, took me there one evening. We had trolled Tom Mack lures for cohoes around Lesquite, had our limit of fish and Doc wanted me to see Hornby.

"I like the place because it's so fantastically wild," he said. "It supplies me with the kind of therapy I need for my work. These islands have it. I cannot explain it, they just have it."

Seeing that I was eager, he started up his two 18 h.p. motors and swung his beloved 16-foot fiber glass *Pacific Mariner* toward Hornby.

As we approached the island, great numbers of birds were seen clinging to the rocky cliffs. They were black cormorants and were nesting. Besides the thousands that clung precariously to the rocks an equal number with only heads protruding outward occupied holes and other crevices in the cliffs. "I hate to disturb them," Tom said as he cut the motors, "but watch."

He clapped his hands several times and yelled, "Hey, you guys, what goes on there!"

Instantly the birds began dropping off the rocks and taking to the air, shrieking as they went. Those inside the holes soon followed. In a matter of minutes the air all around us was filled with thousands of noisy, frenzied birds, giving the impression of a monstrous avian bedlam. The sun had set and the milling of the birds in the evening twilight resembled a great bat flight. The scene gave us an eerie feeling. Tom apologized to the birds, turned on the motors and headed for a special point on the island.

Hornby is treeless and strange. Much of its barren surface is pumice and volcanic ash, suggesting its recent origin as an igneous extrusion. We landed our craft on a black gravelly sandbar and went ashore, examining grotesque rocky forms, crushing clinkers and volcanic beds of ash. For a moment we imagined ourselves as being on a crater of the moon.

The tide was out, exposing numerous dark watery caves overhung by cliffs. We crawled down into one of them and, with torchlight, examined great quantities of green surf grass. The cave was full of flat-bladed brown and palm tree kelp. Out in the deeper water of yet another cave we spotted several red sea urchins. In other caves, in still lower tidal zones, we encountered encrusted sponges, hydroids, bryozoans and several kinds of small darting fish. Left stranded in the tide basins were tiny shrimp, jellyfish, and minute forms of parazoa and metazoa. Here and there potholes were filled with trapped small herring, prawn and crabs. As we scampered back out and into our boat, a bewhiskered seal broke into view, coughed, blinked its eyes and then disappeared. As we started to leave we rode over a large bed of floating brown kelp and noticed a "herring boil." The fish made a living soup out of the sea and the silver salmon were having a feast.

The abundance of marine life on and around these islands is perfectly amazing. Here the herring is a key factor in the food chain of much marine life as well as land wild life. But clear water is basic.

The herring is a plankton feeder and when herring gather in great schools it is largely because food is present. An upwelling from the set bottom brings to the surface a "green pasture" of plankton and the herring, being surface feeders, gorge on it. Then upon the herring gorge the salmon and other fish and upon those feed the gulls, terns, cormorants and other sea birds, seals, porpoises, and the toothed whales.

Plankton, for the most part, are minute plants and animals. The most numerous plankton organisms are plants. These may comprise considerably over half, perhaps as much as two-thirds of the plankton take. Most of them are simple primitive plants consisting of a single cell. They are chiefly algae and, of these, diatoms are the most common group. Some 1500 species of diatoms occur in fresh water. In salt water there is an even greater variety.

Under a strong magnifying lens or a microscope, a diatom is an exquisite thing to study. It is encased in a transparent "pill box" of glass-like silicon, beautifully etched with lines and pores. Like grass and leaves, diatoms too contain green chlorophyll and are thus enabled to utilize the sunlight to synthesize carbohydrates from the inorganic substance in the water. In spite of their chlorophyll, however, diatoms look yellow-brown under the microscope. A similar form, the desmids, which occur in fresh water, are a bright green. These and other minute chlorophyll-bearing algae are the basic food makers of both salt and fresh water. No plankton animals, nor plankton feeders, nor animals that feed on the plankton eaters could exist without them.

The diatoms and other plankton plants are capable of rapid multiplication on a vast scale. Individual species recur in rhythmic cycles, at times actually clouding the water with their numbers. Some idea of the enormous quantities of individuals present is gained from accumulations of their cases which fall to the bottom of the sea when the diatoms die. Some of these great beds of diatom cases, now fossilized and raised above the water, form masses of "diatomaceous earth," 40 to 100 or more feet thick, and several miles long. The city of Richmond, Virginia is built on such a bed.

Plankton animals differ even more than plankton plants in degree of complexity. Nearly every phylum of the animal kingdom is represented. There are the one-celled protozoans—the foraminiferans, radiolarians, and dinoflagellates; there are many jellyfish-like medusae, hydroids, and ctenophores, there are crustacea such as copepods, ostracods, amphipods; there are tunicates and many others. In addition to these permanent plankton forms, there are the eggs and larvae of fishes, starfishes, sponges, worms, mollusks and larger crustaceans that "drift" through their infancy as plankton. These temporary plankton animals form quite large seasonal populations; one codfish, for example, lays ten millon eggs a year, and a single mussel will do the same.

Although most species are microscopic, plankton animals vary in size from the jellyfish which may be three or four feet across, to one-celled forms so tiny that they filter through the finest silk.

The greatest concentration of plankton during the day is some little distance below the surface. In the ocean it is often fifty or more meters down. At night, however, there is usually a vertical migration of the plankton toward the surface. This is accompanied by a similar migration of fish and other plankton-feeders. Schools of herring may often be seen swimming at the surface at night. Some special food studies of the herring reveal that the stomachs of 240,000 herring captured daily for a period of three weeks contained an average of 10,000 copepods, a common plankton crustacean. Along with the herring may come seals and small sharks which in turn feed on them.

The gills of herring and other plankton-eating fish are especially adapted for straining out these tiny organisms. The larger toothless whales, the right, finback, and the great sulphur-bottom whales, feed almost entirely on plankton, extracting it by means of their baleen or whalebone.

To better understand the amazing life found on and around those sea islands of the Pacific Northwest, a brief look at the physiography of the region seems appropriate. Without some knowledge of how this region came to be the way it is, the resident of the area or the visitor misses a great deal.

Geographically, the Pacific Northwest covers all of Washington and Oregon, parts of California, Nevada, Idaho, and coastal British Columbia and Alaska. Although five major provinces dominate its geography, it is the Pacific Border province which seems especially fascinating. It is here where you find a picturesque blending of sea islands, mountains, valleys, lakes, glaciers, rivers, and evergreen forests —a montage of nature such as exists nowhere else in the world.

Sharply dividing the region from north to south is the so-called Cascade Sierra province, a rugged, mountainous area with some of the wildest and most picturesque scenery in America. East of here is the Columbia Plateau province with its fabulous volcanic lava flows, said to be the second largest in the world. Eastward lie two more provinces, the northern Rocky Mountain and the Basin and Range provinces.

Each of these great provinces has its special land forms and characteristic plant and animal life. But each also has its ties with its neighbor, a delicate interrelatedness in land and life which is comforting to see. Although I find much that is appealing in each province, it is the coastal island region that has attracted me the most.

One cannot help but notice the profound influence of the sea in this northwest country. After all the Pacific is our greatest ocean, covering some 71 million square miles, a great seascape teeming with life, from microscopic plankton to giant whales. The Pacific Ocean pushes against this part of our continent with three powerful currents—the Alaskan, which moves south along the west coast of Alaska and through the Aleutians; the North Pacific which sweeps directly eastward and then turns northward in an arc as it hits northern British Columbia and lower Alaska, part of which is deflected southward; and the California current which hits Vancouver Island and coastal Washington and spins southward. These currents are largely surface water movements and, being warm, exert a moderating influence on the coastal areas. The reason central and southern British Columbia has a warmer climate than coastal Oregon and California is due to these currents and the fact that California and Oregon have an upwelling condition which brings cold ocean bottom water to the surface.

The Pacific Northwest is new, geologically speaking, dating back only 20 million years when the Cascades first began to rise; they are still rising. During this period the tremendous lava flows developed and covered some 200,000 square miles to form the Columbia Lava plateau. These lava flows spread about in many directions and changed the course of rivers and streams. Then, only 1.2 million years ago, when volcanic eruptions reached their maximum, a chain of "fire mountains" was left, which is what one sees mostly today. While rivers and erosion have done much of their work in the past million years, cutting up the country extensively, other factors like the ice age, one million years ago, caused extensive glaciers to form on tops of the mountains. But a warming period in the last 10,000 years has left only remnant glaciers here and there on tops of the highest mountains.

The coastal islands of the Pacific Northwest are noted for their great variety of plants and animals. This is largely due to the great influence of the sea and to the great variation seen in elevation, climate and soil. The coastal shore area, bays, fjords, and mouths of rivers and streams form favorable habitats for marine life. Inland lakes and rivers support other forms of life. The evergreen forests, some with up to 120 inches of rainfall a year, give rise to still other forms of plants and animals. Up in the high mountains, arctic alpine conditions support still another kind of community of plants and animals, making both the island region and its closely related mainland an area which can be legitimately called a "nature paradise." The State of Washington alone has over 3,000 species of plants, over 300 species of birds, and no fewer than 130 species of mammals. On one mid-May Audubon field trip to Mt. Rainier, I was able to count 140 different species of trees, shrubs, and wildflowers, and 85 western birds. Several days later, a trip to an intercoastal island, gave me a record of 157 plants and 95 birds. Some of the plants and birds I saw on the two different days in two contrastingly different worlds were the same. Most, however, were different because they were in two different life zones—one in the so-called arctic-alpine life zone and the other down in the transitional and Canadian life zone.

On the larger coastal islands that support mountain ranges several life zones appear, very much as is the case on the mainland. So size is a factor of relatedness, the larger the island, the more its fauna and flora seem to approach that of its nearest land mass neighbor.

Pacific coast sea islands, in many cases, are still wild. Even those which are sparsely inhabited, like Vancouver Island, have much natural and wilderness quality about them. Islands like Guadalupe and the Channel Islands off Southern California have herds of seals, including the huge elephant seal which measures up to 20 feet in length and weighs up to four tons. Oregon has innumerable small headland islands that hug the coast, inhabited by great colonies of sea birds who find them sanctuaries from various land predators. But it is Washington and British Columbia and Alaska that have the extensive island country, ranging from the great number of small emerald-like islands in the straits (Strait of Juan De Fuca and Strait of Georgia) to the great islands of Alaska, including the Aleutians. Islands like Kodiak and Attu are world famous, as are the Pribilofs with their great herds of fur seal.

Rocky sea islands also occur in great number along the northeastern American coast from Connecticut to Maine and northward. Here the islands are much older environments with a correspondingly more advanced plant life and more soil. The shores of these eastern islands have been worn smooth over the ages as strong seas have done their work. Here one often sees tide pools which have been scoured out of solid rock and shoreline caves polished smooth like glacial potholes. Around these eastern rocky ramparts there is much mixing of currents and waves, of churning and upwelling, of tidal undertow and washing, all of which attracts sea life above and below the water's surface. Fish are abundant—cod, striped bass, pollack, and halibut. Here the anadromous alewife and shad find a favorite habitat for feeding. Porpoises ply the island shores in search of fish, and many birds, eiders, mergansers, a dozen species of gulls, terns and other sea birds are after the leavings.

An unusual island off the Maine coast is Mount Desert Island. Perhaps nowhere in northeastern coastal America is a small island region so packed with scenery and amazing geology. The mountain is not lofty —only 1532 feet above sea level—yet it is the highest point of coastal land on the Atlantic Seaboard north of Rio de Janiero.

Just when Mount Desert Island was created in its present form is a point of discussion among the students of geology. However, the island is a wonderland of creation. The traveler gets his first glimpse of the wonders of Mt. Desert Island from the mainland, when he sees the mountain range rising out of the sea.

The Island is a wonderland to be sure. It has, for students of geology, collectors of minerals, or lovers of nature, a wealth of earth history to be read and appreciated in its miles of exposed rock masses. The history is written here and is easy to read for those willing to learn the language. Take, for instance, the pink granite domes which make up the mountains. These were thrust up under a layer of mud which was a part of the floor of the sea. The molten mass cooked this to sandstone and slate. Ages of erosion removed this upper layer and left the granite exposed. The whole range of mountains (Monadnocks) was split and filled by new intrusions. The best is visible in the cut on the Mountain Road. A wide band of black diorite or basalt is exposed and easily studied. The green epidote veins at the Thunder Hole or in the "pot holes" below the crest of Mt. Cadillac is another example of recorded history. The same material is found in small veins across the entire range. The white quartz dikes above Hunter's Beach is another example. All these show some of the changes which occurred there.

The greatest record written in the local rocks was put there by the glacier which pushed its way over the area and over the tops of the whole range. This glacier left scratches on the rocks that are still visible and yet its greatest feat was the cutting of a channel through what is now Somes Sound. The great weight of ice cut and wore a path through a small mountain valley and wore it away until it had made the only true fjord on the continent (except for the Hudson River Valley which some people claim is also a fjord.)

There are important lessons to be learned from sea islands. These are often brief and cryptic, but many are long and drawn out and full of meaning.

A little more than a hundred years ago a stooped, slim Englishman named Darwin shook the world with a revolutionary theory. Perhaps more than any individual scientist he put man and nature into a new perspective. He did it with the sensational book *The Origin of Species by Natural Selection,* based upon a study of plant and animal life in the Atlantic and Pacific Ocean areas, particularly the distant offshore Galápagos islands west of South America.

Five years of scientific study aboard the British ship *Beagle* gave Darwin a mass of evidence to show that there exists in plant and animal forms an evolutionary principle—a gradual developmental pattern from one form to another—which, until then, had never been demonstrated or proven to exist.

Returning to England with a mass of data, Darwin went to work diligently compiling a book. Twenty-three years later his published works rocked the world back on its heels. Seldom in recent times has a single publication caused such a violent reaction among people or such an impact on science.

Charles Darwin showed by massive proof that life processes vary considerably in plants and animals and that new forms are often produced. He revealed that oftentimes these new forms are better suited for survival under certain geographic and climatic conditions than the original kinds. Plants and animals which possess traits more suitable for survival under specific conditions, for instance, will tend to perpetuate the species. Those lacking such traits in sufficient quantity will tend to die out. A form may develop traits so completely unsuited to the environment that death will come quickly. Such life forms possess, so to speak, too large a dose of the lethal traits. This, in a brief way, is the substance of the famous and widely accepted doctrine of *the survival of the fittest* and the *process,* biologically speaking, is referred to as *natural selection.*

The important lesson one can draw from *The Origin of Species* and Darwin's subsequent book, *The Descent of Man,* is that undisturbed sea islands are often repositories of great scientific fact. Unspoiled they can be great storehouses of natural history data, and so should be preserved. Darwin showed that all living things, including man, are inextricably tied to their natural environment and that they survive or perish as they are able to adapt themselves and live in harmony with their changing environment. In the process of adaptation new and more complex forms of life originate. There is in nature also the gradual and steady evolvement of a species toward a higher and higher form of life. A species either does this or it dies out. Islands at sea, therefore, serve man as ecological samples of nature—as it was and continues to be.

The Sandy Barrier Islands

In contrast to the rocky islands of the Pacific and northeastern Atlantic coasts, we find the so-called sandy barrier islands—those largely composed of sand and mud and silt. The barrier islands of the mid-Atlantic and Gulf coasts are low-lying, somewhat elongated environments. Normally they lie just outside the mainland zone and undergo constant change, for they catch the full sweep of ocean currents and tides. Lashed almost continuously by winds, often of gale and hurricane force, their character is varied and constantly altered. One northeaster I know about cut away a thousand feet of a frontal beach; another drove a new channel across a sandy island. A third ate away a great chunk of sea beach, only to turn around and add an extension to another island. I once rode out a gale which gouged out a quarter mile slough along Virginia's Cobb Island beach, to the delight of surf fishermen. Deep swales with single outlets to the sea or those with double ends are the favorite hangouts of fish and fishermen. Into these freshly made ravines come hungry fish to feed during the rising tide. The angler knows this. Thus when a surfman sees a typical slough on the beach, his heart swells with hope, for he knows that sometimes remarkable fish come into such places and tackling a big fish can change a man's life.

Some years ago I was fishing a beach slough on a barrier island when an incident occurred which cannot be forgotten. My companions were Heath Clarke and Gilbert Larus. We had stationed ourselves over a long stretch of beach and were waiting it out with peeler crab as bait, and the tide was rising. All of a sudden a fish struck my bait, hung, and began struggling. As Heath was nearest to me, I waved my hat toward him to gain his attention. Surely he might enjoy watching me land this fish. Heath noticed my signal all right and returned a hand wave but made no effort to come over. Chagrined, I went to work on my fish and after about 15 minutes beached a ten or twelve pound black drum. Again I waved to Heath but to no avail. He only waved back and continued fishing.

Some time later, with my bait gone, I stopped fishing and decided to join Heath and replenish my bait supply. Approaching the point where he was fishing and with my black drum dragging in the sand, I called out, "Hey, Heath, why didn't you come over and watch me land this drum? He's not big but was fun catching."

Heath, a slight old man, glanced over his shoulder and squeaked out in a tired voice, "Couldn't do it, man. Got one on myself. Been on an hour. Reckon he's ready to come in?"

"Ready to come in! Now, quit your kidding," I spouted.

"No, no, I'm not kidding. I really got one on—been on an hour and he's still fighting. Come see for yourself."

Excited, I dropped my fish on the sand and rushed over to Heath to see what was happening. To my astonishment Heath *really* had a fish. What was even more amazing was he had no more line on his reel—not an inch.

"Great Christopher, Heath," I cried, "here, give me your rod. Let me get some line in, quick. If you've got a big fish, this is no way to handle him."

Heath was all tuckered out and a little relief seemed welcome. I reeled in about 75 feet of line and then handed the rod to him, saying, "Go to it, now, Heath, bring him in." Then I yelled to Gilbert to come over. This was too much.

Twenty long difficult minutes later the old man maneuvered a beautiful red gladiator, a channel bass, into the foaming surf and Gilbert and I rushed out and grappled with it like a bear, finally carrying it bodily to the beach. Utterly exhausted, Heath flopped down on the beach beside the fish and sighed, "Mercy, what a big fish . . . what a fighting . . . powerful fish."

The fish was an average-sized channel bass or red drum, tipping the scales later at 33 pounds, but it fought Heath a total of one hour and twenty minutes, giving him the most thrilling battle of his seventy-year life.

An hour later action broke again. I whipped down my first channel bass which weighed 35 pounds. Next day Heath and I again caught one more each of the same size class. This made four channel bass apiece, plus one black drum. Gilbert Larus had several good strikes and one fish on but lost it. All the fish came from one slough.

So thoroughly exciting was this experience that it launched me into surf fishing and island visitation in a serious way. As for Heath Clarke, it made a new man out of him. Months and even years later, whenever I would see him, he'd grin, shake his head, and nod silently. I knew perfectly well what he was thinking. He was reliving, as he had so often relived since the big event, one of the great satisfying experiences of his life.

Sandy barrier islands, like those in Del-Mar-Va (Delaware, Maryland and Virginia) are the favorite gathering places of flocks of gulls, terns, and shorebirds. The gulls are the common herring gull and the laughing gull, with a mixture of others thrown in. The terns are largely the royal, Caspian, and the common tern. Sanderlings are the most frequently seen of the shorebirds, dancing everywhere on the sandy beaches as if playing tag with the spreading surf.

Two species of barrier island birds which seem to take over the islands are the willet and the black skimmer. The willet is a large shorebird, 14-16 inches long, with white patches contrasting with blackish on both surfaces of the wings. On the islands it puts up a noisy *pill-will-willet* when disturbed.

The black skimmer, on the other hand, is neither a shorebird nor a gull but an island bird of extraordinary uniqueness. Most people call this strange, odd-looking, coastal bird the shearwater or scissor-bill, largely because of its peculiar beak. Others speak of it as the storm gull because its anxious shrieks are supposed to warn watermen of an approaching storm. The most popular name seems to be plain *skimmer*. This is because skimming is what the bird does best—over water with the ease and expertness of a pelagic sea bird.

On many occasions I have watched these birds skim so close to the water that a mere downward dip of the head will cause their beaks to cut the water for a short distance. The skimmer is such an unusual bird that ornithologists have placed him in a family all by himself.

The skimmer's beak is remarkably specialized. He literally "plows the main" with his bill. In Del-Mar-Va where I have observed the birds for hours on end, their food consists of fish, small crustaceans and clams. The lower mandible is a third longer than the upper and acts something like a canopener or pair of scissors when eating food. The entire beak, sharp as a knife, is flattened vertically instead of horizontally like that of a duck.

Another unique feature of the bill is that the upper mandible is hinged at the base to facilitate opening and closing of the mouth from above. Half crimson red at the base and half black, the entire bill seems so incomprehensible that one wonders how it works. Yet function it does, with remarkable efficiency.

I find skimmers exceedingly fascinating to watch at work, for they make good company while fishing on lonely barrier islands. True to their name, they prefer quiet ocean surfaces, often backside waters, where the gathering of small crustaceans and mollusks is easier and more rewarding. When searching for food in earnest, they can be seen gliding over the sloughs or surf, mouths open, cutting the water back and forth, back and forth, heads sometimes snapping back in a quick jerk as a hard object strikes the lower mandible.

The skimmer is known for a remarkable deed, the picking up of a hard clam, carrying it aloft over some hard surface, like a road or rock jetty, and then dropping it, only to return to feed on its broken contents.

As proof that skimmers were found in the early days along our eastern shores, Henry A. Purdies quoted old natives of Cape Cod to the effect that "them cutwater or shearwater birds used to be with us summer times." Though never valued much for feathers or flesh, the eggs of skimmers were long prized by fishermen because of their size. A well-formed skimmer egg from a mature bird will measure an inch in length. Since skimmers deposit their four white and buff eggs on the bare sand, without concealment, many would-be families are destroyed along our northeastern coasts. In the early days before egging was made illegal young boys and watermen used to collect skimmer eggs for the market.

"Gul aeges . . . gul aeges for sale," used to be a common vendor's cry in the streets of Charleston and other coastal towns.

In my travels to island country, I have seen skimmers along the coast all the way from New York's Jamaica Bay Wildlife Refuge southward to Florida and the Gulf states to Texas. The birds prefer to winter in the warmer climates and have been found from the Gulf to the northern and eastern coasts of South America. Of the five species in the skimmer family which inhabit the temperate world, only one, however, the black skimmer, is found in the United States.

Skimmers seldom go very far inland, nor do they travel far at sea. During migration time in the spring, I have seen them in large flocks, often numbering hundreds and on occasion thousands. During this period, they are a restless lot and their peculiar nasal barking and squawking fairly drowns out the boom of the crashing surf. Were it not for the black skimmer, our Atlantic barrier sea islands would not be the fascinating worlds of nature they still are today.

All too often today in coastal areas man flaunts nature in the face and then cries for help. In the Colonial days the settlers seemed wiser. They did not settle on low, exposed seaside islands but moved up the rivers and inlets to locations that gave them not only protection against the harsh elements but also access to richer soils and a chance to establish large plantations. While they still made much of their living from "the water", they kept a safe and respectful distance from it.

Today man so often disregards the principles of natural law discovered out of experience and builds bridges, roads, houses and places of amusement right along the sea's edge or on barrier islands. Little wonder then that unusual storms, northers, easters and hurricanes, often wipe such developments clean with much loss of human life. Low-lying sea islands should not be developed any more than one would develop the top of suspicious volcanos. The value of barrier islands lies in their functional role of protecting the mainlands—for man and all other living things that share the natural world with him.

A vivid illustration of what can happen on a low sea island makes me recall a near-disaster on Metompkin Island, a small low island on

Virginia's Eastern Shore, northeast of big Parramore Island. To reach it, as with most barriers, one must go by boat. The island is exceedingly flat and is surfaced with low myrtle bushes, smokeweed, seaside goldenrod, and waving spartina grass. A lonely Coast Guard station commands its eastern end but, its small gallant crew, the casual visitor seldom sees.

It was late in September one day when two companions and I planned a three-day campout on Metompkin. Our mission was a hoped-for rendezvous with big channel bass.

We pitched our tent on the highest point of land on Metompkin, a spot which bore no sign of high water. All gear and supplies were carefully placed inside the tent: cameras, bedding, groceries, and the usual odds and ends that go with a camping-fishing trip on a beach.

The hour was mid-afternoon and the sky had gradually turned into a pale mackerel. The wind shifted to the east and began blowing harder. But the urge in a surfman's heart is strong, so with gear and bait in hand, the three of us took off for the eastern point of the island and its open beach. After a mile or so of plodding we came upon a promising protective slough and stopped. It was our only hope for channel bass.

For hours the bitter northeaster gave us its worst but we stuck it out. Nightfall came. The tide was in flood and continued flooding. When it did not stop, we grew nervous. At last a second sense told me to call it quits and begin the long trek back to camp. Night descended quickly like a gray-black sheet. Now the wind was a lashing gale, hurling great rows of breakers against the beach, shooting salt spray all over us, and creating an eerie whiteness along the shore. The tide kept on rising. Higher and higher it rose. Suddenly, in the light of a great breaker, we could see that the whole island was turning into a frothing sea.

Sensing a dangerous situation, we veered away from the beach and plodded knee-deep in water across the highest point of the tideline. Eyes straining to locate the easiest route, the going was difficult. One by one we sank into big holes, going down into water up to our necks.

Every step was labor now. When Eddie, of our threesome group, went down to his shoulders for the tenth time, I really began to worry.

Finally, the Coast Guard crew at the station somehow sensed our plight and turned on their beacon light. The scene was astonishing. The whole island was now a flooded angry sea. Only the tufts of marsh grass here and there stood out above water. We dragged on toward a black object at the far end of the island. It was our tent—it stood half submerged in sea water. Inside, everything was afloat. To retrieve anything was hopeless, so we zipped up the doorway and left it to the flooding sea.

Back at the station the guardsmen were yelling something in the wind and beamed a powerful light in our direction. Water was everywhere. Inch by inch, foot over foot, we felt our way through the cold brine toward the station, water in our waders squashing at every step. Finally, dog-tired and wet as beavers, our feet touched higher ground. Soakingly we dragged our frames onto the station's main base, water streaming from us in long sheets.

"Close call, eh," said the Guard petty officer. "Island floods sometimes. But tonight's storm is the worst we've seen for a long time. How about some hot coffee?"

An island that is a different kind of barrier land mass is Sanibel. Its reputation comes from seashells. It is an island in the Gulf of Mexico, just off Fort Myers, Florida. Until recently you could go there only by ferry; now there is a 3-1/2 mile causeway. At the outer end is the "Seashell Capital of the World". You can walk along 10 miles of coast line and often see only continuous seashells.

Conchologists and marine scientists come to Sanibel from all parts of the world. Most contrive to arrive during the first full weekend in March, when the annual Shell Fair is held in Community Hall. In the arts division there are trays, tables and pictures created by the arrangement of shells. There is jewelry, some produced from almost microscopic specimens. Most coveted award is the one presented by Philadelphia's Academy of Natural Sciences.

Since Sanibel is a year-round art colony, the annual fair also

features a "clothesline" display of paintings and camera art, all by local residents. Usually the Audubon Society also has an exhibit of rare tropical plants collected on the island and adjoining Captiva Island.

That week, even fair visitors join the dawn patrol of Sanibel Benders along the beach. They are up at the first suggestion of light to see what the night tide has washed up. They walk in a bent-over fashion that is known as the Sanibel Bends.

Everyone carries a bucket. Some carry authoritative books as there are more than 400 varieties of shells washed up here. Some carry shovels and dig, dig, dig. The shells are not just on the surface. They are deep. No one knows for sure how deep. A commercial front-end loader can dip out shells all day long and load them on trucks. Next morning the location can hardly be discerned; the night tide has filled the space.

Once all of this was life. Once all of these creatures were alive in the sea, and died there. There probably is more ex-life on Sanibel's beach than the number of all humans who ever lived on this earth through all time. How long has this been going on? Milleniums perhaps. These creatures lived and died and the earth moved on and on without them.

Coral Islands

Sea islands also are composed of coral. Also low-lying, these islands are creations not of physical elements but of creatures of the sea. Mostly flat with only low ridges appearing above sea level, such islands are often characterized by massive growths of mangroves along their edges. The central substance of these islands is not sand, not granite or volcanic rock but the skeletal remains of once living animals—animals which, when alive, were able to transform certain chemical substances of the sea into rock.

Coral islands and living coral reefs which surround them or to which they are closely associated are found in tropical seas where the water temperature rarely drops below 70°F. This is due to the fact that the builders of coral structures, the coral animals, can only perform their amazing task in warm water. Coral protoplasm converts sea water calcium into coral reef substance. Corals do not occur along western

coasts, where there is deep, cold water, caused by upwelling and cross currents. Thus the California shores and the Pacific coast of Mexico lack corals, while the Caribbean waters support them in abundance. They are common also to the waters of Brazil, the tropical coast of eastern Africa and northeastern Australia, where the Great Barrier Reef and its coral islands form the largest geographic structures of animal life in the world.

The only coral islands and coral reefs in the United States are the Florida Keys. These remarkable islands stretch out for 200 miles and are a naturalist's paradise. The Keys have a dual nature. The eastern chain is mangrove in character and in origin are the tops of coral reefs born during the last glacial period. The western chain is studded with pines and myrtle bushes with bases of limestone rock formed from solidifying sea drift laid down in an interglacial sea. Some of these islands, like Big Pine Key where the remnant Key deer are struggling for survival, have risen only slightly above the surface of the sea.

Life in and around coral islands is perfectly amazing. On the drier Keys tropical and semi-tropical wildlife abound. In the thicker vegetated upper Keys countless birds—wood storks, various herons, pelican, and coot—find ideal habitat. In the shallow shore waters play game fish: bonefish, weakfish and others. Around the mangroves tarpon prowl in great numbers and snook wait for prey at night. In the deeper Gulf Stream waters such sport fish as sailfish, barracuda, dolphin, bonita, grouper, wahoo, and amberjack are commonly seen.

Out away from the vegetated islands, on the living reefs them-selves, a fantastic collection of animals live in perfect harmony. One group takes over by day, another takes over by night. It is a world of fantasy, color, strange light, feverish activity, violence, repose and tran-quility. It is a world largely hidden from human eyes, but a world wait-ing to be explored.

The coral polyp is a minute, carnivorous, night-feeding animal that is related to the jellyfish, but in reproductive habits and growth more nearly resembles the oyster. It appears in myriad forms, and the colonies which grow on the reefs represent an almost incomprehensible number of individuals. The shells of the dead animals when piled one upon the other in uncountable billions, combined with the skeletons of other calcareous animals and plants, are responsible for the great masses of the reefs. The reef masses in turn become the home of countless vari-eties of colorful sponges, anemones, sea whips and fans, worms, shrimp and spiny lobsters, to say nothing of the vertebrate fishes. Among these are grunts, snappers, parrot fish, and many varieties of angel fish of breathtaking beauty. Such is the variety that new species are being found and classified constantly, and it is apparent that many years of research lie ahead if the secrets of the sea reef are ever to be fully dis-closed.

On the Bahamas and Florida reefs, the most troublesome under-water creature for man is probably the spiny sea urchin. Skin divers and snorkelers must be wary. These animals, active hunters at night, spend their daylight hours in the myriad holes and crevices of the coral. They can be easily seen, looking like great black pincushions, and while they are not equipped for aggression, they can inflict a painful wound if stepped upon or brushed with the hand. Underwater enthusiasts should be warned of this and other dangers.

The moray eels, which attain a length of five or six feet, likewise live in their coral hideouts, and will most surely remain there unless dis-turbed. But the diver should learn not to reach into a coral hole with-out careful reconnaissance.

The coral reefs are areas of endless variety. Their beauty is superb.

Knowing something of them is at once an experience of the deepest satisfaction and a challenge of some magnitude. There is so much to be known about them, and all of it can be exciting.

But coral islands do not stand alone. For the most part they have strong ties with other realms of nature and the strongest of these are those with the seashore world—that amazing frontier of the mainland where two great worlds merge.

SEASHORE FRONTIER

THE WORLD BY THE SEA IS A RESTLESS MONTAGE OF MANY MENTAL images: a bright morning sun illuminating a vast ocean plain; sea oats and beach grass rustling in the wind; noisy gulls and artful terns searching out the rising tide; the hypnotic swell of ocean waves and the steady boom of crashing surf. It is creeping fiddlers by day and venturesome goggle-eyed ghost crabs by night, barnacles and periwinkles patient and expectant and waiting—all waiting for the periodic refreshment by a mother sea. The seashore is sea otters playing among the rocks and silver salmon feeding around the kelp beds. It is wary multicolored creatures on the reefs and the stir of incredible life forms in abandoned pools of sea water. It is the spellish rise and fall of ocean waves and the distant cacophony of ever-moving and ever-pounding seas. All are scenes that remind us of a region of unsurpassing enchantment, deep meaning, and great natural beauty.

The seashore world is a strangely alluring environment, drawing life to it like some hidden magnet. So strong is its appeal that once the visitor has tasted it, he keeps returning again and again, each visit more satisfying, each encounter more enriching. Ever-changing, yet somehow, in some indefinable way, steadfastly changeless, this world by the sea is an enormously balanced and stable place—a world that exerts its influence landward and seaward far and wide and almost endlessly.

The seaside natural world is a lavish place. So amazingly varied and so uniquely perfected and productive is life along the shore that no human can fully comprehend it. And in no other living environment, in no other ecosystem on earth, is life more complex or more beautiful or more bizarre or fragile.

But to know this most marvelous of worlds, one's inner senses must be attuned to its ways. One must learn its many comings and goings and its innumerable and dramatic events which occur daily behind the scenes. A beach sojourner cannot really know the beach until the bathers leave and the wild creatures, the true owners, take over. Moreover, one should be willing to observe natural events and things closely and to interpret what he sees correctly and, if possible, be willing to advance a measure in knowledge. To become familiar with the sea's origin, the ways of tides and waves and ocean currents, or the wondrous moods of the elements, or to become familiar with the amazing diversity of living things along the sea's edge, is to become a follower of this fascinating world. Thus, the visitor or the resident who becomes moved by the sun as it slowly sinks below the ocean sky or is awed by the violence of nature as opposing currents do battle on a wind-tossed shoal, is one who, in some unexplainable way, has trained his senses to behave in harmony with the universe.

To know the seaside environment is to experience first-hand the therapeutic value of a soft oceanic breeze, or feel the hot summer sun on a dazzling beach, or to know wet rain or cooling fog on one's face in the early morn. To appreciate the power of a seaside storm is to ride out a northeastern in a dinghy or hear a beach cottage creak and strain in a hurricane. The price for these and similar experiences runs little in dollars, but it does require a willingness to explore in nature and a commitment to careful observation. Seeing rather than just looking comes well rewarded in the seaside world. Often, on a solitary walk, one can be a witness to strange performance: sand fleas burying themselves in the wet sand, sanderlings dancing fancy ballet steps beside the incoming tide, a crab striking away at a passing killifish. And on occasions the compensation for patience can be a once-in-a-lifetime experience, like the sighting of a rare bird, or the lightning flash of a barracuda against a wounded mackerel, or the sudden surprise of a huge wallowing shark at one's feet.

My own life as a biologist forked many years back when I ventured out to sea in a rowboat to fish for flounders. It advanced through several decades of visiting beaches and over the years became strong with the pursuit of surf fishing as a weekend pastime. Finally, when I was treated to a thrilling piscatorial encounter—catching my first big channel bass—my attraction for the seaside world became intense, deep, and soul-satisfying.

The serious observer on the seashore soon becomes aware of the amazing fact that here is an environment with enormous amounts of life. It was, after all, here in this motherly kingdom where life first began, where most living things developed. Here one can sense quickly the long history of relationships between sea water and the bloodstream of life. Not only did the sea give rise to the many plants and animals now found there, but also to countless other living forms which left its borders to inhabit the land—to dwell on coastal and offshore islands, over sand dunes, to live in the marshes and swamps and grasslands, in the forests and deserts, and to flourish even on the mountain tops and on the Arctic tundra.

Of all the places on earth where plants and animals live, none is richer, none is biologically more productive, more varied, than the waters of the seashore. Here lies the favorite habitat of innumerable simple plants and animals, the diatoms and protozoa and numerous higher invertebrates, such as the jellyfishes, worms, mollusks. Here also is the world of countless vertebrates, the fishes, birds, mammals. Here are found seals, porpoises, dolphins, and large whales, including the largest of all mammals the world has ever known, the great blue whale.

The places where the land and sea merge, be they rocky or sandy, packed with silt or laden with mud, are showcases of nature and the twentieth-century sojourner, watching the ice floes and other objects move relentlessly down our rivers to the oceans of their birth, cannot help but marvel at what is taking place. Here is nature's exhibit of a great frontier.

The rivers of our earth have always carried ice, mud, sand and gravel to the sea's edge which, in settling, have spread layers of sediment over the sea bottom. Remains of various forms of life, such as shells, accumulated after death in these layers on the ocean bottom, where their hardened parts became preserved as fossils. Over long periods of time, these great sediments consolidated into hard rock and were elevated above sea level to form land areas.

The scientist of today studies the seashore and the ancient sea deposits, which now form a large part of the earth's surface. From the character of the sediments and from the life remains or fossils that they contain, the geologist is able to reconstruct much of the past history of our planet.

The rocks in the earth's crust give evidence also of the physical conditions under which they were formed. Apparently the physical processes, such as erosion and weathering, have not changed throughout time. The life on the earth, however, is constantly varying, owing to a changing environment, and species after species sooner or later dies out to be replaced by another form. Rock formations of a similar age, therefore, contribute similar species of fossils. Human history, which is measured in thousands of years, is but a small part of historical geology, which necessarily extends back through many millions, even billions of shadowy years.

A noted geologist was once asked what would have happened if all the sedimentary rocks of past ages had been accumulated in their thickness in one place. He replied that they would have formed a succession of strata 40 miles in height. In some cases this is exactly what did happen. This succession, known as the geological column or timetable, is constantly being referred to by the geologists in life history studies of the earth.

The earliest activities in the earth's geologic history are believed to have been the results of chemical and physical processes. It is believed by some that the first form of life was a one-celled plant (probably formed in shallow sea water), and from this primitive form of life, all other forms of life developed. Thus through the ages there arose many plants and animals of the past and present, culminating in the age of man which dates back some four million years when Primitive Man was said to have lived on earth.

One can picture the various ages of geologic time as a great pyramid. The heavy, central base, occupying five-sixths of the entire pyramid constitutes the era of the Primitive Crust. Then came the Archeozoic Era, the age which gave rise to unicellular life, followed by the age of the marine invertebrates, or the Proterozoic Era. The age of higher invertebrates, the shelled animals, came next and became labeled as the Paleozoic Era. The Mesozoic Era followed and was succeeded by the Cenozoic Era, or the age of mammals and modern plants. Man, a comparative newcomer, came to occupy the top of the pyramid in a period known as the Psychozoic Era.

Little is known of the earth's history during the period of the formation of the primitive crust. Dramatic events no doubt took place, but no eyes were present, no ears were around to hear or to record what was taking place. For perhaps half of the five or six billion years from the early formation of the earth to the origin of unicellular life in the sea, there was incredible dead silence. There was only the period of long, silent epochs with enormous fireworks, gaseous convulsions, spinning gases and atomic explosions. It was also a period of cooling, hardening, and much rainfall.

Then, in some distant watery world, perhaps where the soft land masses met the warming waters of the sea, strange dead-looking substances began to take on the appearance of partial life. Again and again it happened. One day, however, perhaps two billion years ago, the first living thing, a bizarre but full-fledged unicellular plant, took shape and assumed the functions of what we call life.

Because early plants and early animals had no tough fibers or bony skeletons, little record of their life was made in the rocks. One can only try to guess or imagine what took place.

It took the trilobites who lived some 500 million years ago to record in stone the early life of creatures on earth— a record as dramatic and long-lasting as any living event on earth. So numerous were these small shrimp-like arthropods that they filled the tepid seas around the globe, spreading a vast blanket of seething, shell-rustling life everywhere. They entered every seaside shelter, every cove, every lagoon. Billions upon billions of them came, out of the deeper seas, out of the shallows to fill the bays and mouths of rivers, creeping and crawling and piling up staggering waves of crust-life forms on the shortlines.

The trilobites ruled the earth for a hundred million years, yet no living trace of them exists today. Gradually, over millions of years of living and dying, development and counter-development, they vanished, only to record their presence in fossil rock.

The age that became dominant after the trilobites was that of the nautiloids, small and large mollusks, some measuring fifteen feet across, creatures which today are represented by some 800,000 species.

The shelled animals gave rise to the sea scorpions, a strange set of animals closely related to our arthropods, the insects, spiders, and crayfish of today. These odd sea animals were the first creatures that tackled the land frontiers. About this time the continental shorelines buckled and great cataclysmic upheavals shook the land, rolling back the seas. Stranded on drying sands, imprisoned on mud flats, the scorpions died by the billions, but some survived. And those that did survive multiplied into prodigious hordes. Some grew large, reaching nine feet in length; others were much smaller, only two or three or four inches long, and turned their long antennae landward. Inch by inch, yard by yard they crawled about and began devouring the dwindling trilobites. Onto the shores they crept, over the hot, dry sands, into the steaming marshes, one over the other, swarm over swarm, into fern-filled swamps and over and across ridges and higher escarpments. For thousands and millions of years they came—a total of forty million years—writing a record of a land invasion by sea creatures in the pages of Silurian time such as the world had never known. Today, however, only in a few places can one find evidence of this great era of the earth's exciting, once crustacean-dominated history.

Today, the visitor to the sea's edge, unless he be familiar with the earth's geologic timetable, misses much of the great exciting story of a wondrous world long past. Yet if he is only partially curious, he may find interesting examples of another epoch. One such clue of our earth's link with the past is the horseshoe crab. This relic from the past is common to the Atlantic coast from Nova Scotia to the Gulf of Mexico, but most abundant in Delaware and the other mid-Atlantic states. The horseshoe crab is not a crab at all but an arthropod, similar to the scorpions that first took over the seashore world. It is a true throwback to the post-trilobite era. When one looks at a horseshoe crab he is peering back hundreds of millions of years into history.

Today, as in early times, the seashore world continues to be the gathering zone of remarkable forms of life, some strange and beautiful, some fantastic but all naturally wondrous.

The sea's edge is dominated by two great phenomena: the amazing reproductive potential of marine organisms and the seemingly ruthless predation with which one form of life lives at the expense of another.

A good example of the fruitfulness of seashore waters is the sea nettle. In the Chesapeake Bay the sea nettle, also known as the common jellyfish, often becomes a seasonal nuisance. One week the bather can joyously swim in the bay without concern, the next week he is appalled by what has happened and must trade swimsuit for rubber boots. Almost overnight, the bay has literally exploded with sea nettles. Jellyfish are everywhere. Then, in a few weeks, when the main reproductive cycle is over, the strange animals disappear. Once again the bay seems free of them. But the freedom is only from the so-called jellied stage of the sea nettle, as the germ cells persist in the polyp, only to give rise the following summer to another massive generation of sea jellies.

As for the question of eating or being eaten, it need only to be said that the phenomenon of predation is a natural and persistent biological reality and no amount of headturning or shunning will change it. Nature has built into its system of checks and balances the principle of one life form existing at the expense of another. The process is most dramatically illustrated among the larger animals, such as when a barracuda slashes away at a wounded Spanish mackerel, or when a pack of killer whales attacks a leopard seal or charges against a member of their larger blue whale cousins. Predation, then, is a normal event which occurs throughout the animal kingdom, from the minutest of life forms to the largest, and man sits on top of the food pyramid.

Most naturalists prefer to view predation in terms of food chains, envisioning the process in terms of the building blocks of life. At the base of the food pyramid we find the diatoms, trillions upon trillions of one-celled tiny plants with bizarre, silicon frameworks which form the "green pastures of the sea." These great blankets of floating microscopic plants and animals are collectively known as plankton. Some of the plankton animals feed on the diatoms, but generally the plankton support higher animal forms which, in turn, sustain still higher and larger kinds of animal life—sponges, worms, mollusks, crabs, fish. At the top of the pyramid are sea mammals, like the seal, whale, and finally, man.

Generally speaking, the larger the animal, the greater the protein requirement to sustain it. Some marine animals require prodigious amounts of food each day. There are salmon, for example, that eat their weight in herring every three days. According to one noted biologist the humpback whale—which is not the largest species—consumes at one meal about a ton of herring, roughly 15,000 fish. Each six-inch herring in turn may contain 6,000-7,000 small crustacea in its stomach, each of which again may contain as many as 130,000 diatoms. In other words, some 400 billion yellowish-green diatom plants are needed to sustain a single medium-sized whale for only a short time.

I once witnessed the reduction process on a 39-foot California gray whale. It occurred in San Francisco Bay and what came out of the whale's seven-foot stomach was utterly amazing: shrimp, cod, squid, and what looked like barrelsful of whole herring.

Life along the seashore for the most part is astonishingly fleeting, varied, and not without its surprises. Sometimes, when the traveler least expects it, a combination of events can take place which make for a life-remembered experience.

If one wishes to start learning about marine natural history, the

but an animal. Another crab, this one a lady crab, comes into view. Directly beneath it sprawls a baby horseshoe crab and here and there is a patch of Irish moss. Suddenly a small school of killifish flashes by and the rock crab strikes quickly with its big claw, but is too late. A small six-inch sand perch appears and dashes its jaws into the sand, wriggling, and pulls out a sandworm and quickly engulfs it; a bay scallop shell is dusted with residue sand from the scuffle.

Such is the drama in a marine arena embracing a single square yard of shallow intertidal sea bottom. Yet it is enough to set your mind to wondering, and wonderment is the thing the sea's edge provides in considerable measure.

Continental United States alone has 54,000 miles of shoreline while the North American continent has a staggering 140,000 miles of coastal shore. The land masses of the world enjoy perhaps a million miles of shore country, and every mile is a place of interest. Everything along the seashore frontier, from the magnificent sweeping beaches to the rocky headlands of the exposed coasts, has something to offer the serious student or the casual visitor. And every foot of sand and every rock, every mud flat is worth one's attention and scrutiny.

One of the more interesting of places for seaside exploration is the New England coast. Another good place is Cape Hatteras. The sparkling white beaches around Daytona, Florida, are also good. Another spot worthy of a visit is the Sanibel-Captiva area west of Ft. Myers, Florida. Anywhere along these remarkable beaches one can find a fantastic amount of life if he but takes time and does some modest searching.

One day on one of these beaches I chose to cut through the beach sand with a shovel and see what I could find. With a small spade I cut vertically down across two feet of the wet intertidal beach and then sat down to study the cross-section walls. The discovery was amazing: shells of every kind, whole and broken; worms, sand fleas, ghost shrimp; tubes and openings and burrows of ghost crabs and countless small marine organisms that were not possible to identify. From this simple study I became convinced that here on the beach was a living, bustling Lilliputian megalopolis, really a minuscule city of countless inhabitants, working, living, eating, digesting, or unconsciously waiting to be eaten. Here, then, was not the dead beach that it seemed, but a complex thriving world of countless animals living out a strange and fragile life along the edge of the sea.

I finally covered up the trench in the sand and began strolling the beach again and in doing so, couldn't help but feel that I was walking on the delicate rooftops of millions of tiny marine creatures and that I should walk respectfully and softly over them. The sandy beach was their fragile home.

Our seashore creatures run into the thousands of species. In a general way, the numbers are overwhelming. Yet only to the close observer do many forms truly reveal their secrets. So, close observation should be the watchword in learning about the seaside world.

At Point Lobos on California's Pacific coast, for example, one can observe hardy sea otters at work or play. The casual visitor can watch these rare and interesting creatures for hours upon end, be delighted and refreshed, yet may still go away not much better acquainted with sea otters. But if one really studies them closely, he may discover some unusual talents among these animals.

One day along Pacific Grove a scientist tried this. He watched several sea otters dive for sea urchins and return to the surface, there soon to perform a very remarkable operation: opening sea urchins on their chests and eating them. They did this by banging the morsels against rocks which they had placed on their own chests. When a sea otter dove to the sea for a live sea urchin, he would pick up a flat rock from the bottom, carry it aloft together with an urchin, place the rock on his chest, float on his back, and then begin this remarkable feat. The trained ear and eye can catch the banging sounds and see the incredible operation take place—a mammal using tools to carry out a feeding process. The sea otter is one of the few living creatures in the world which has the intelligence to use objects to carry out a difficult task.

Perhaps the most valuable singular quality of the seashore world is the spiritual refreshment it gives to man. Everywhere, the world over, men seek the seaside world for solitude and the recharging of their fading spirits. People walk to the sea, drive their cars to it, or bicycle to the edge of the sea to seek out its deep strength, for from the seashore, from its blue-green waters and the sky, the sea stretches endlessly and gives out a great source of refreshment.

The sounds of nature by the sea are therapeutic and people come to hear them, waiting alone, or in pairs, or groups, watching or quietly strolling, every person solemnly eager to capture every note, absorb every combination of sounds. Even the most strident, most violent of the noisy elements, are soothing to the ear and men brave them for the goodness they bring. In essence, the seaside world is a symphonious world and men wish to be attuned to it. But this place by the sea can also be wild and terrifying.

Perhaps the three most awesome sounds in nature are the earth-deep bowel rumblings of a volcano, the howls of timber wolves at dusk in the northern bush, and the sounds of a violent sea at night on a lonely beach.

And nowhere in America is elemental nature so bewitching as at Cape Hatteras. Here, a mercilessly-exposed sandy elbow of land, thrusts itself out to sea a good thirty miles, affording the visitor priceless opportunities for bold experience. Separated from the mainland by vast, unprotected Pamlico Sound, the cape with its incredibly thin, long wings of shifting sand, receives the fury of rampaging nature: winds and gales and hurricanes, two powerful-but-opposing ocean currents, frequent lashing rains, and virtually a constant pounding of beach sands by titan breakers formed far out at sea. Nowhere in the temperate world is a fragile ribbon of land more exposed to the encircling sea and nowhere does a beach receive greater punishment from the wild elements.

Dubbed by mariners long ago as the treacherous "graveyard of the Atlantic," where more than 600 ships have gone to their watery graves, or where they became grounded on the dangerous hidden sands of Diamond Shoals, Hatteras is the essence of unbridled nature.

One usually finds what he seeks and if it's adventure, Cape Hatteras has it. This recklessly-exposed region, so packed with history and drama, has moods in full measure and the captain who sees storm clouds forming over the cape and does not pull sharp rudder can expect trouble. Even the new islander who fails to heed the telltale clouds is soon sorry. All who come here must abide by nature's warning signals or take the consequences.

It is not easy to put into words what Cape Hatteras is like when she takes the full fury of a northeast storm. I have been to the cape many times, have watched the cold Labrador Current do pitched battle with the Gulf Stream, one cold and racing south, the other warm and moving north and the impact of their meeting hurling enormous sheets of water high into the sky.

So powerful are the gales at Buxton Point that one must lean a strong 30° into the wind to walk on the beach. Yet at times adventurous surf fishermen, impelled by some strange magnetism, stand there on the exposed point hour after hour and take it. Sand-blasted, wind-blown, they hold a lonely vigil on a lonely beach, waiting and hoping that some piscatorial giant will take their mullet bait and literally drag them out to sea.

To know the full terror of an Atlantic storm at such a place is to live out a wild northeaster here in the fall of the year. The worst I ever witnessed came on the heels of Hurricane Hilda when she slammed her fists into the coastal face of Louisiana but, soon thereafter, began casting gales at Hatteras.

I had come to the cape with a companion, Byron Ashbaugh, to take pictures and to experience the climb of the highest brick lighthouse in the world. After struggling and puffing up 283 howling stairs, my friend and I found the top of the lighthouse a weird and dangerous place. It was virtually impossible to move out onto the terrace because of the near-hurricane winds. Yet, pushed by the spirit of adventure, we were determined to claw our way to the outside. As we progressed outward, the lighthouse quivered and shook like a huge vibrator. Around us the sounds were one great roar, like the falls of Niagara, only we seemed to be right in the thick of it. Holding on to

the protecting bars of the railing, we managed to ease our way around the terrace, but the wind was so penetrating that our eyes watered out in great streaks and we couldn't see. Soon a massive chilling entered our bones, so we didn't stay, much less attempt to take pictures. We descended the stairs only to discover that down on the beach the whole character of the cape had changed. Darkness closed in quickly. We took refuge in a rented cottage not a hundred feet from the lashing sea and there chose to spend a strange and exciting night.

The winds gained in intensity and their force and sound had changed. Now the roar of a massive waterfall had become a hissing whine in a lashing rainstorm. Out on the front porch a lone wooden rocker was feeling the storm. Each time a great gust of wind hit the cottage, it shook violently and began rocking. But soon it steadied itself, only to react again to a massive blow.

As the night wore on, the storm increased in violence. At one point a looping thunderous blast hit us and the lights flickered. The pictures on the wall rattled. Water poured in under the door. My companion went for a bath towel and began soaking it up. Then, suddenly a second tremendous blast hit us, savagely shaking everything inside. It began as a long, drawn-out muffled roar, came on fast and closer and then lost itself in a deafening crash, shaking us and the cottage and earth around it. It felt like ten thousand tons of water had been dumped upon us at once. I sensed it was the slow build-up and sudden death of a monstrous wave.

"Great Christopher, that was a big one," I said to Byron. "Let's go out and see what that one did to the beach." Normally such invitations would be received with ruffled eyebrows, but my eager naturalist friend was willing.

We slipped into rubber waders, pulled over ponchos and, torchlights in hand, went out into the eerie night. Outside, a fierce gale-driven downpour was beating against the cottage. Descending the wet stairs carefully, we buffeted our way along, stung every inch by great gusts of wind. Slipping our way up a small sand dune covered with planted sea oats, we paused for breath, water streaming down our hoods as if from a roof. Upon reaching the top of the dune, we stopped again, peering out across a violent sea. The beach was an indistinct mantle of patterned blackness and a whitish frothing foam. Squinting into the night, I could see breakers forming across the outer sand bar—first one, then two, then four great swelling horsemen, rising and rushing forward, then each rolling into one huge curl. Then came the tumbling and the roar of great falling surf.

Fortunately, the tide was ebbing and a shallow slough had developed between us and the dangerous surf. Boldly, we advanced toward it. But distances are deceiving at night and one judges objects to be farther away than they really are. Experience, however, had taught us to move cautiously at such times, to stay alert and use all senses. In the light of our torches, we could make out the outlines of large windrows of flotsam, that wet, mixed-up aftermath of the receding tide. Sloshing over to it, we halted, stooped down and began examining object after object: seaweed, grass, small and big chunks of driftwood, hundreds of black empty egg cases of the skate, shells of clams, mussels, scallop and much cockle. Here and there were string-like garlands of whelk and the broken up remains of spider crabs. From one large pile of debris we dug out several sea cucumbers, a giant starfish, and one stunned, cold, thoroughly confused and out-of-place freshwater amphiuma or Congo eel. The storm had washed the strange amphibian out of a nearby freshwater pond and carried it to the sea.

We turned off our torches and stood immobilized for a moment, absorbed in the strange blackness. The surf continued crashing violently up and down the beach and the wind swept up and sand-pitted our faces. Through watery eyes, I could see a whitish sand bar out in the gray-black night. The sea's temper was cascading over it, sending out one thunderous roar after another. As each breaker smashed itself over it, a swishing sound spewed itself white in front of us and cut loose a spray of seabrine. Again and again the wind beat sand into our faces and rain pellets, like bullets, hit our parkas. Every 15 seconds by my watch, revolving big Hatteras light illuminated the beach momentarily, only to leave us quickly once more in strange darkness—alone again in the wild night, alone with the wind and the rain and the merciless sea.

A man feels small and insignificant in the face of such violent nature and reacts to safety accordingly. The slough in front was deep and treacherous. One quick slip into the fierce undertow and there would be trouble. It was too risky. Flashing our torches once more and, in the silence of deep thought, we began walking slowly over the wet sand toward the friendship of the cottage. We had savoured nature's violence at Hatteras to the full.

But the seaside world is also a tranquil place. Often there are scenes of unsurpassing natural beauty. There are brief moments when the surface of the ocean is like a great sheet of glass. Nothing moves, nothing stirs. The mood is deep, pervasive, and the sojourner who stops and waits for these calms can be absorbed by them and filled with a penetrating spirit—a feeling as deeply moving and uplifting as perhaps anything on earth. Like the great stillness of a cathedral, the tranquility of the sea seeps into one's bones, reaching the innermost fibers of the soul.

In beauty, the seaside frontier can be a place of indescribable natural loveliness. Although each of nature's wild environs has its own special charm, it is the world by the sea that stands out in unmistakable splendor. In poetry, in painting, photography and literature, it seems that it is the great diversity and marvelous beauty of the seaside world that shines forth.

Beauty, of course, is a perception created by one's mind. What is beautiful to one may not be so to another. The beauty of the seaside frontier may well lie in the thing called balance. When there's balance and harmony in nature, there's congeniality, and then the quality of tranquility seems to flow. Thus, when all seashore qualities are brought together in just the right measure, the quality of beauty is strongly manifest. So if we want more natural beauty in this world and in our lives, we should be willing to save some of the natural places that engender it, and at the same time, teach more people to perceive it. The edge of the sea is such a place.

SAND DUNE COUNTRY

LIKE THE KNEE-CAP OF A BENDED KNEE, CAPE HENRY LIES NAKED ON Virginia's coast where the Atlantic is wedded to Chesapeake Bay. One spring morning in 1607 a band of adventurous colonists landed on this cape of sand, erected a wooden cross to mark their visit, and then sailed on. A day later they found the James River and followed it to Jamestown Island where shortly they established the first successful English settlement in America.

No one knows for sure what emotions swept through those courageous men and women who made this historic landfall. One can only imagine. But surely the sight of the cape and its majestic dunes—those quiet and beckoning hills silhouetted against the western sky—must have quickened every heart aboard.

From the three small vessels, the *Sarah Constant, Discovery,* and *Good-Speed,* they could see the windswept trees, the fresh green pines, live oaks, holly, and bay. Silent, immutable and brooding, the hills lay before them, their yellow summits a mass of loose, drifting sand. It was a strange sight to behold in one sense, but there is no doubt that all aboard waved to the dunes as they sailed on by—paying a thankful tribute to having set foot on the first soil in the new land.

Since that eventful day in April, more than three and a half centuries ago, many changes have come to Cape Henry dunes. In the years just before World War II, one could still see the remains of what was once great dune country. Its beauty was still distinct, although desert-like. From the top of one of the highest hills, one could see an area of land and sea and sky strangely different from any in Virginia, a veritable small Gobi Desert in a seascape of semi-tropical loveliness. The shore country nearby was bathed by soft breezes from a surfless sea and the sky was always the shade of the blue Mediterranean. All around the cape was sand, great mounds of it, piled foot upon foot for a hundred feet. There were small mounds, large drifts, and prodigious hills of shifting sand. And there were acres of barren landscape where nothing grew—nothing except occasional stunted trees and these stood waist-deep in sand, as if buried by snow.

One could gain the summit of a sand hill and stand in silence while grains of moving sand swept past your feet. Down along the fringes of the dunes tufts of beach grass waved in the wind. Some tufts were living, but most were parched and dead, dried brown like grass in the desert. You could think about the animal life on these hills and their slopes and their bottoms. A man or boy could plow down a summit slope and see the gray remains of dead things: skeletons of fish, crabs, and numerous empty shells, and it was apparent that a high-flooding northeaster had been here and left its mark on the dune country.

One could rest, and then climb once more to the top of another large dune, and out of breath, gaze down upon a rolling sea—and listen. Beyond your heartbeat, you could hear the mixed symphony of many seaside sounds, all in tune with wild nature: the whine of the wind through the pines, the voices of shorebirds along the beach, the rustle of dry shifting of sand at your feet. And every so often there would come the rhythmic boom and crash of the surf on the cape. It was a beautiful and refreshing sight, but also disturbing, for already on several sides, you could detect the telltale forces of human encroachment at work.

Today the Cape Henry dunes are almost gone. Civilization's heavy

heel has brought destruction and spoilage to much that was lovely and historic. Most of the area is now off-limits to the public as a military reservation has taken over practically all of the land. Large portions of the beach that once displayed solitude and whistling winds now are lined with houses. A priceless stretch of dune country which once knew only the action of wind and tides has been usurped and mangled by monster military vehicles, all practicing mock run sea-land maneuvers. Many of the larger dunes were cut down and levelled, and their dark sand bases sold off as lots. Houses and cottages now sprout in places where loblolly pines and holly and live oaks grew.

When the dunes were alive, excited boys and girls from a nearby 4-H summer camp used to romp over them. They had fun. The loose sandy summits were goals to climb. From these high places one could see unique formations of sand and strange kinds of plants and animals. Even a leisurely saunter up a single sand dune was well worth it for, next to snow, as every boy soon learns, it is sand that offers the best medium for the study of animal tracks. Here in the dune country were conditions for natural history study that rated "just about perfect." On some days in the summer a sharp eye could count no fewer than a score of familiar animal tracks. There were many fox tracks. Because of their size and depth, they stood out noticeably. Mink and skunk and opossum tracks were less common and those of otter, muskrat and raccoon most rare. But most abundant were the tracks of unfamiliar birds and hundreds of smaller footprints of unknown creatures. Creature foot trails seemed everywhere. And in more than one place a sand trail would lead to a tragic end, perhaps a field mouse meeting its fate as some raptor swept down upon it, the markings of wing beats still visible in the sand. Often one could spot the torn feathers of a quail as it, too, met its fate at the hands of a predator.

In those earlier days reptile trails were especially evident during the warmer months, their winding trails clearly visible around the base of every dune. One afternoon a group of six urchins followed the tracks of a tiny lizard. After some 50 yards of tracking, they saw where it had tried to take refuge in the den of a ghost crab, only to be dispatched there by an ingenious raccoon. They learned the principles of checks and balances at work here on the seemingly sterile sands of what looked to them to be a forgotten world.

The Cape Henry dunes were always worth an hour or two of exploration and those who loved them kept returning. But it was something deeper than a mere romp that kept many coming back to the dunes. Why did they come? Was it the plants? Was it the animals? Was it the sounds? One suspects that it was all this and more—the delicate mixture of peace and serenity of the singing dunes themselves, their beauty and their strange aliveness.

Around the turn of the century when photography was still rounding out its development, a certain sensitive Frenchman, known only by the name of Mann, made periodic visits to the Cape Henry dunes to record on film their remarkable form, as well as their hypnotic mood. That he succeeded in full measure is attested by the striking photographs that came out of his camera. Using old-type, 8x10 glass plates, he produced some of the most artistic photos of dune country ever portrayed.

Restless Dunes

Sand dunes all over our continent present a puzzling contrast against the living landscape and the dunes of Cape Henry and others along the sandy Atlantic coast are no exception. Even when these seaside dunes appear as barren ghosts against a leaden sky, they are wakeful and stirring and very much alive. Over their windswept crowns there is ceaseless change and constant movement. Over every inch of a dune's nakedness there is a slow, imperceptible driftage—wind-driven fragments—consisting of calciferous shell granules and bits of rock. All are restless. Grain upon grain they roll and pile up, row upon row they pile together, mound upon mound, rolling, settling, now piling up into ripples and rows and grotesque sandy escarpments.

But the dunes are not free, for they are handcuffed to the wind and, with this shackling agent, they grow or wither and die. Without wind, dunes are soon stabilized and grow old. Live sand dunes, wherever they occur, are young, and to stay youthful, they cannot remain still. Sharp pointed one day, round the next, dunes get long or elliptical, like an egg. And they pulsate like a vital organ of some prostrate body. Today you see them as blunt, odd-shaped forms, next week, they are flattened muffins spread out on a bake pan. Ceaseless change is their watchword.

With change, of course, comes a shift in plant and animal life. Down in the depressions, a steady struggle goes on to stabilize the sand, one force to hold it, another to turn it loose again. Grasses emerge and take hold, but soon are buried; shrubs sprout, but are covered over; and trees which stand in the way of the moving sand are soon engulfed to the crown; and further still, sessile animals that cannot escape sand driftage are entombed in great mounds of sand.

Often when the sojourner tramps the sand hills and sees his footprints filling with sand, he is reminded of those wonderful lines in the Book of Ecclesiastes which, more than any other passage in Biblical literature, seems to capture the rhythm of ceaseless change in our living world:

One generation passeth away, and another generation cometh: but the earth abideth forever.

The sun riseth, and the sun goeth down, and hasteth to his place where he arose.

The wind goeth toward the south, and turneth about unto the north; it whirleth about continually, and the wind returneth again according to his circuits.

All the rivers run into the sea; yet the sea is not full; unto the place from whence the rivers come, thither they return again.

Jockey Ridge

One of the last great dunes along the Atlantic coast today is Jockey Ridge in North Carolina. This unique, somewhat incongruous land of much sand and sky, is situated between Kitty Hawk and Oregon Inlet along the "outer banks" at a place called Nags Head. The sandy ridge is so strangely spectacular that the visitor may wonder why it was never included in the Cape Hatteras National Seashore. Yet it never was, and today this noblest of all Atlantic sandhills is going the way of the Cape Henry dunes.

Jockey Ridge is not a vast place. Measuring about nine square miles in area, it is neither too large nor too small to be invulnerable to development. Its highest two points are magnificent dune heads. One is a kind of big brother to the other, but both breathless in their paradoxical beauty. No other dune on America's east coast is higher or commands a sharper appearance; no other hill of sand sends the heart to stirring more. There are secluded spots on Jockey where you can see nothing but sand—only great convolutions of drifting clean sand. If ever one felt like being in the Sahara, he feels it here, in this remarkable region of overpowering sand.

From the high crown of Jockey Ridge one can see and on rough days hear the great Atlantic surf as it pours out its nostalgic boom and crash from Kitty Hawk to Oregon Inlet. On clear days the ocean and sky seem one. Like vast blue blankets stitched crosswise by windrows of white breakers, the sea rollers swell, then curl and finally crash in a torrent of foam, spreading whiteness all along the beach. The spell is magical and seems to enter the very marrow of your bones.

Dawn on a Dune

One October I made a special trip to Nags Head to see the dawn come to this sand dune country. As I started my trek across the sands, the heavy orange sun was just beginning to lift its head out of the gray Atlantic. Progress over the loose sand was slow and my legs began tiring quickly. Several laughing gulls careened overhead and protested my solitary advance over what seemed their legitimate domain. There were terns about also, Caspians and royals, and they shrieked in the distance where the surf and sand met sky.

Soon the sun was out to its full and promptly began to radiate its warmth over the desert-like landscape. Now, everywhere, the sands began to glisten. Reaching the first of the two sand ridges, I turned around and sat down. The sun and the sea were dazzling. I stretched back on the sands and closed my eyes, and soon a heavy sleepiness overtook me.

How long I napped I do not know. But when I awoke, great pillows of clouds were moving swiftly across the blue sky. I sat up and unconsciously began passing my hands through some sand.

Now sand is sand to most people and so it was to me until this moment in time on Jockey Ridge. Then I commenced to think seriously about it. How much sand makes a handful? How many sand grains can one hold in his hand? How many sand grains make up a whole dune? And why do sand grains stick to one's hand in spite of violent shakes to remove them?

These were intriguing thoughts and I pondered over them. Then I reached in my pocket for a hand lens and began a little study. Those sand grains were worth examining. I turned on the most powerful of the lenses and began trying to count the individual granules clinging to my hand. It was incredible. In an area smaller than that occupied by a pea I counted well over 300 sand particles. How many more would fill a tiny bundle the size of a pea, there was no telling. Surely the number might easily reach several thousand.

Most of the sand particles seemed to have rough edges and I surmised they were shell fragments and therefore marine sands. Others bore smooth surfaces and seemed polished like gems from a polishing tumbler, obviously quartz in origin. Apparently the wind and the sea had combined their work to make these sand grains into perfect microscopic quartz gems.

Again I scooped up a handful of sand and let it all fall through my fingers, shaking away all that would go loose. Again my palm held millions of grains of sand—sands from the rocks of Maine, the Adirondacks, the Poconos, the east slopes of the Appalachians. These were sands carried by the rivers to the sea and there mixed with shell fragments, churned and buffeted, and finally thrust upon the land to be dried by the sun and picked up by the wind to help form Jockey Ridge. If only a grain of sand could speak, to tell its story, it would be a tale which would shrink to nothingness the greatest land and water voyage ever made by man.

These grains of sand were not quartz fragments, but marine sands, spawned at sea and released by the sea. That nature should pile up such an immense mixed-up mass of sand with trillions upon trillions of tiny grains of rocks and shell fragments, particles once belonging to the earth's rock or to sea animals, all different in shapes, and none of the same composition, seemed short of unbelievable. Yet here they were, grain upon grain, on North Carolina's Jockey Ridge—proof of an amazing phenomenon of nature.

Sand dunes wherever they occur suggest a kind of incongruous unreality. They are dead and yet very much alive. Even when they appear as the very personification of the desert, they exude a vitality and viability more profoundly alive than other hills of the earth. Even the most arid of these seemingly lifeless wastes show a wakefulness that is hard to believe. Marching, always marching, fresh dunes have been known to expand the deserts, to bury great edifices of man and to engulf cities and bring desolation to vast green landscapes of thoughtless people. Whether they occur along coastal waters both salt and fresh— America, Australia, Africa—they have a restlessness not common to other undulating surfaces of the earth. Were we not to have them, the earth somehow would be robbed of a very special kind of beauty.

Water-related sand dunes occur along the entire Atlantic coast from Cape Cod to Florida. The Gulf coast has small sand dunes in Texas although many of these are now stabilized. The most famous dunes along the Pacific coast are found in Oregon where a desperate battle is being waged to save them.

The Great Lakes shore country is also marked by dunes. The Indiana Dunes near South Bend and Great Sleeping Bear in Michigan are noteworthy. They are classic examples of America's lakeshore landscape and need to be saved.

Inland Sand Dunes

Less than an hour's drive northeast of the small Rocky Mountain community of Alamosa, the nation's highest inland sand dunes poke 600 feet into the southern Colorado sky and spread out for miles—10 miles to be exact—like a roiled tawny sea.

In this rarefied air of the San Luis Valley, the sun-and-sand diversions usually reserved for the seashore dunes can be found—and all in the shadows of the 14,000-foot high Sangre de Cristo mountains.

The graceful, wind-rippled mounds are the heart of Great Sand Dunes National Monument, established in 1932 by the National Park Service. A favorite camping spot for travelers "roughing it" in the Southern Rockies, the monument is reached by taking State Route 150, which veers off State Route 17 about 13 miles north of Alamosa. The route is entirely paved.

Late spring to early fall is the ideal time to enjoy the outdoor activities, historical mementos and natural attractions offered at the 57-square-mile monument, which is open the year round. On any clear day, however, the site is visible from 70 miles away. It is seen as an incongruous panorama of bleached sand, whirled and whipped into delicate patterns, against a backdrop of towering blue mountains.

During the busy tourist season the dunes are bright with the variegated hues of summer apparel, including an occasional bikini among the Capri pants. The weather is normally bikini-oriented, so much so that one must assiduously guard against sunburn.

Barring a maverick thunderstorm, only the unflagging breeze mars the climate. Even when the wind currents are mild, a sojourner can find himself walking through an ankle-deep sandstorm. However, geologists say the relentless southwest winds are responsible for the very existence of the freak sand dunes.

In explanation, they point out that the San Luis Valley itself serves as a trap for the sand particles. To the east and northeast lie the Sangre de Cristos. To the west, toward Durango, are the picturesque towering San Juan Mountains, and to the south, the San Luis Hills. A natural "catch basin" is formed, with its mouth to the southwest, the direction of the prevailing winds.

For hundreds of thousands of years, geologists say, these winds have picked up sediment deposited by mountain streams flowing into the valley. As the winds reach the northeast corner of the valley, they must rise to get through the three passes in the area. They lose velocity and the sand then falls to the ground to be added to the great hills already there.

In recent years, photographs show, the dune mass has changed its location very little. But the ceaseless winds are constantly sculpting, shifting, sorting and piling new designs and contours all within a confined area. Photographers, who are advised to come early in the day—or late, when shadows and highlights accentuate the outlines— find the monument extremely photogenic. This sand dune country is full of textures, patterns, tones, colors, and moods.

A Visitor Center and museum are open from 8 a.m. to 5 p.m., and admission is free. Accommodations are limited to a campground and picnic area furnished with wood, water and tables. Provisions and gasoline can be obtained at Hooper and Mosca, 25 miles to the west on State Route 17, and at Alamosa.

Each morning at 8:45, a ranger gives a brief description of the monument at the picnic complex north of the Visitor Center. And at 9 a.m., a naturalist conducts a tour.

At any time, visitors can take the Montville Trail Tour, a nature study through a small valley. The tour begins at the registration desk and requires about 30 minutes. Numbered stakes correspond to a guidebook supplied at the Visitor Center.

The first stop is at the location of the old tollhouse and stage station for the Mosca Pass Toll Road, built under the charter to the state in the late 1800's. The road eventually fell into disuse. A severe thunderstorm in the early 1900's washed it out completely, and only a trace of it can now be seen.

From the tollhouse-stage station site, the trail leads out through an arboretum of both desert and mountain plants, including skunkbush, sumac, mountain mahogany, piñon, snowball cactus, cottonwood, soapweed, mountain snowberry, and Douglas-fir.

Zebulon Pike, for whom Pikes Peak was named entered the San Luis Valley through Medano Pass in the winter of 1806-07 and mentioned the dunes in his journal. The explorer, John Charles Fremont, used Mosca Pass in 1848. Later, other explorers, including John W. Gunnison, viewed the dunes and wrote about them.

The dunes are separated from the Visitor Center and camping areas by Medano Creek, a small, meandering stream that flows principally when the snow is melting in the mountains. In summer, one must usually wade through its clear waters to reach the dunes.

A small quantity of sand has blown across the creek, forming an area of little dunes. This area, with its ghostly, skeleton-like trees that are smothered and then exposed as the sand comes and goes, is a graphic exhibit of the fate of vegetation here.

An egregious fate for the dunes themselves was briefly considered during World War II. The monument was one of five sites studied as a test area for the explosion of the first atomic bomb. The test eventually occurred about 500 miles south, in the desert north of Alamogordo, New Mexico.

Another famous mountain sand dune area is found at White Sands, New Mexico. This vast area of white sand is, for the most part, a testing ground for missiles and other explosives but large sections remain open for exploration. These dunes are among the whitest found anywhere in the world.

Wind and Sand

Whether on seashore, lakeshore, mountains, deserts, or rivers traversing arid lands, it is the constant wind that builds up sand dunes.

When winds scud along the earth's surface, they pick up fragments of rock, shell or coral, drop them, pick them up again, dashing one particle against the next and usually making the surfaces smooth. The tiny sand grains are blown about and if some obstruction breaks the sweep of the wind, the sand grains are dropped, accumulating in masses from small ripples to giant "whalebacks" 100 miles long and weighing millions of tons.

Most sand dunes are composed of quartz, which is one of the most common minerals on earth and a silicon dioxide which occurs in colorless, transparent or colored hexagonal crystals. Other dunes are formed of other materials such as gypsum, lava, coral, and basalt.

Sand dunes take on many shapes—the longitudinal-shaped dune and the crescent-shaped barchan, the shorter transverse dunes, pyramidal and star-shaped cones, and the parabolic or U-shaped hills whose crescent tips point into the wind.

Live dunes are active dunes and they constantly alter their form and position. Sand particles are swept up the more gradual windward slopes, tumble over the crest, and roll and settle on the leeward side. In this manner a whole dune can move or march in the direction of the wind and progress from several feet to as much as 300 feet a year. Sand dunes have crept over forests and suffocated them, have covered swamps, farmsteads, roads, railroads, and cities, both in America and Europe. The old cities of Acre, Tyre, Totlusa and Laodicia have been smothered and entombed by marching dunes.

Dunes can get to be very large, reaching upwards of 900 feet in height, as we have described in Colorado, 700 feet high in Saudi Arabia and Iran, and 1,000 feet on the Great Sahara. But dunes are quite rare. Despite what most people think and what motion pictures show, most deserts are not sand dunes but barren rock. Drifting sand covers only one-seventh of the Sahara.

THE MARVELOUS WORLD OF THE MARSHES

"THE MARSH IS AN ENTIRE WORLD IN ITSELF ON THE WORLD OF EARTH —a different world which has its own life, its settled inhabitants and its passing travelers, its voices, its noises and above all its mystery." So wrote Guy de Maupassant, the French short story writer, in the latter part of the nineteenth century. To this perceptive man who composed brilliant vignettes of life, the marshes not only held deep personal significance but great mystery as well.

A half century later another keen observer, Aldo Leopold, wrote: "A dawn wind stirs on the great marsh . . . At last a glint of sun reveals the approach of a great echelon of birds. On motionless wings they emerge from the lifting mists, sweep a final arc of sky, and settle in descending spirals to their feeding. A new day has begun on the crane marsh."

Maupassant and Leopold saw in the marshes, environs of great significance, both to man and all life. But these men lived ahead of their time. Only now are we beginning to recognize how enormously important those herbaceous and treeless wetlands really are.

Let us then look at these much misunderstood and much maligned special worlds as they are and as they deserve to be seen.

Saltwater Marshes

Like coastal islands, seashores and sand dunes, the coastal marshes of America are special natural environments. Were it not for these places and their counterparts, the freshwater marshes, we would have little in the way of coastal marine life and continental wildlife. Certainly we would have fewer ducks and geese, fewer shorebirds, wading birds, gulls, terns and, very likely, no whooping cranes.

Bathed twice each day by the tides, salt marshes form the richest habitat for fauna and flora in the world. Like the marshlands of fresh water they are a special kind of world. They are not swamps. Swamps have trees in them; marshes do not. Marshes are wet lands where the dominant cover is marked by low, herbaceous vegetation—grasses, sedges and reeds.

The salt marsh is identified predominantly by various forms of saltmarsh grass—spartina, phragmites, three-square, eelgrass, and the like. The freshwater marsh, in contrast, is dominated by sedges and cattails. While freshwater marshes are interesting and exceedingly important to inland wildlife, they are short-lived environments and will be considered last. Saltwater and brackish water marshes are old places in nature and once gone cannot be replaced easily. Man can help create freshwater marshes.

To the motoring passerby all coastal marshes look alike. They do not seem particularly inviting and, when the mosquitoes are bad, the quick retort is, "let's get out of *this* place." But a book should not be judged merely by its cover. Neither should a marsh be judged by a single look. If one stops long enough and picks a good day and knows where to go, and what to search for, the salt marsh can be a fascinating and captivating place indeed. Most naturalists know this. So do the bird watchers. Hunters, trappers, and fishermen search out the marshes. They know that a marsh is a great mecca for wild creatures—a kind of a last frontier for fish and wildlife. But salt marshes are even more than this. Physically, chemically and ecologically they form a vital link in our continental ecosystem.

Salt marshes comprise that low coastal country which is imprisoned by the sea, that grassy area between the mainland and perpetual open salt water. It is a watery marine land where the clapper rail sounds his staccato call and the osprey circles in lonely haunts, where the bald eagle screams in fading numbers and the majestic greater snow goose comes in the winter. It is the home of the fiddler crab, blue crab, grass shrimp, gulls and terns, and countless shorebirds. Waterfowl winter in the salt marsh and, in one special location in Texas, it is the southern winter home of the precariously surviving whooping crane.

A zone of prodigious birth, the salt marsh is the breeding ground of the mussel, clam, oyster and countless crustaceans. It is the feeding and foraging pasture of innumerable fish, snails, and myriads of lower forms of marine life. Indeed, the salt marshes are a land of common wealth—a kingdom of such growth and bounty that were we to find ourselves suddenly without it, life on earth would be difficult, perhaps impossible.

There are good reasons why the salt water marsh is a thriving place for plants and animals. Here nature has been most provident in sunlight, food, water, and minerals. Studies show that one square mile of coastal sea water can produce enough nutrients to feed a city of 10,000 people. Brackish and coastal waters are rich in salts, iron, and iodine. Magnesium is especially plentiful. A cubic mile of sea water contains enough gold to fill Fort Knox, or $93 million worth. But the sea does not give up its wealth easily. Practical forms of extraction and harvesting are difficult and oftentimes economically prohibitive. So the gold remains in the salt water marshes.

Salt marshes date back to distant geologic time. It was here, in this kind of an environment, where the early land plants and animals first developed and from whom the higher forms emerged.

Salt marshes today constitute the last great natural land and water kingdom in America. They comprise the last of our extensive unspoiled landscapes of the continent. Paradoxically, tranquil and turbulent, tame and wild, they still embrace millions of partially inundated acres of rich tidewater land and give source to much outdoor recreation. But, as pristine places, they are disappearing fast.

In North America the most abundant salt marshes are found along the Atlantic and Gulf coasts. Others occur sporadically along the Pacific coast and around Hudson Bay, James Bay, and in the Yukon delta in Alaska. In continental United States proper, the most famous salt marshes are those of the delta country of Louisiana, Chesapeake Bay, and San Francisco Bay. Extensive marshes are found in the Del-Mar-Va region (Delaware, Maryland and Virginia), and along the coastal areas of Massachusetts, Connecticut, New Jersey, the Carolinas, Georgia, and Florida. The south shore of Long Island, New York, still possesses sizable areas of marsh country, and some tidal marshes can be found in coastal Alabama, Mississippi, Oregon, and Washington.

To the traveler a salt marsh shows up as several forms. From a car window in coastal Connecticut you may see a polluted tangle of marsh debris and tall reed grass. From a high ridge over the Delaware Bay there sprawls a vast pasture-like grassland, interlaced by marinas and other development. From a plane over Chesapeake country it may appear as winding flatland creeks and twisting rivers—a patchwork of green land and blue water. Not far from Corpus Christi, along the breezy coastlands highway of southern Texas, the salt marsh unfolds like a blanket eastward and westward and is extended like fingers of a hand, each finger a sliver of marsh habitat, each indentation a wedge of Gulf water sneaking inland like a quiet flood. Were it not for the marshes of the Aransas National Wildlife Refuge and other salt flats near by, it is doubtful if there would be any whooping cranes today. The magnificent whoopers, some standing almost as tall as a man, were down to 17 birds not long ago. When I last saw them in 1962 they had risen to 32 and were fighting the most dramatic, most publicized battle for survival of any wildlife in America, except for perhaps the ivory-billed woodpecker which at any moment now may become extinct. These whoopers are a thrill to see. They could have made their last stand in the prairies of the southwestern states, or chosen to make their bid for survival among the rice fields of the lower Mississippi, or the grasslands of the central plains. But they did not. They chose for their final stand the salt marshes of Texas.

Here on the balmy sunshine flats of Aransas National Wildlife Refuge, the survivors cling to life. Here the rare birds can still be seen standing like ostriches, wading, feeding in the shallow-water marsh country, picking up blue crabs, crayfish, frogs, fish, and whatever else they can find. Here on a winter afternoon one can spot a single bird or a pair winging across the yellow-brown salt grass as they move from one feeding area to another. They are a spectacular sight and, knowing that they could be completely gone were it not for their winter habitat, one begins to appreciate the importance of the salt marsh.

In contrast to the whooping crane, a bird that is abundant in the saltwater marsh country is the clapper rail. Unlike the whooper, it is a small bird and, except for its limited seasonal movement, is not considered a true migratory species. Chicken-like in appearance, the clapper has long legs, a long, slightly curved bill, and an olive gray shade which blends deceptively with the marsh habitat. Both the common name "clapper" and the specific name "crepitans," which is Latin for clattering, were given to it for its noisy call which I can only describe as a clattering *cac-cac-cac-cac*. The call is familiar to those who frequent the marshes. The wood-sounding clatter may be taken up and repeated by many birds at one time and may give the marsh quite a clattering racket.

One way to see if clappers are in a marsh is to take a paddle, oar, or board and slap the water hard with the flat side of the object. If clappers are present they will instantly respond with a *cac cac* or two, as if to say, "What was that!" The Pamunkey Indians use this trick on the sora, another rail but which is much smaller than a clapper rail and a frequenter of fresh and brackish water marshes. The sora, however, responds with the fateful *eek eek eek* which is a signal for the gunner to move his pushboat into the marsh.

The clapper weighs from 12 to 15 ounces and is surprisingly secretive for its size. Its home is among the reeds and the spartina grass where it seldom shows itself except at extremely high tides. At such times it will take wing at the approach of a boat and fly a short distance, then drop back into the grass. Its long toes, quick legs, and slender body permit it to dart among the reeds and hide with ease.

The clapper rail breeds from Connecticut south to North Carolina. A few may winter in Virginia but most of them winter further to the south and return to the Chesapeake region, its choice habitat, about the first of April. The nest is made of grasses found in the marsh, and the clutch numbers from 8 to 12 brownish-white eggs, speckled with brown. The young are glossy black, but this soon gives way to the olive gray of the adult birds. The most serious natural enemy of the birds curiously enough is the moon, for it is the moon which is responsible for the excessive high tides in the spring. The high storm tides of the spring and early summer destroy nests and drown the young before they are able to care for themselves. Were it not for the renesting habit of this bird and its high reproductive rate, its numbers would soon be dangerously reduced.

The clapper is heavily gunned during the open season, but fortunately can only be forced from its cover during extremely high tides, and these occur infrequently during the open season. I admire these interesting birds, and have hunted them, but I now prefer just to hear them clatter. One can have no quarrel with the sportsman who takes only his rightful share when there is a surplus, which nature would remove anyway. But one must take exception to the man who fails to play the game fair, such as flushing foursomes and sixsomes from the flotsam at high tide before the birds can take wing, often with outboard running. This is neither gamey nor lawful. It is, in fact, the height of irresponsible license from a moral and ethical point of view and utter inhumanity.

The salt marsh where the clapper rail lives looks flat enough and it is. Yet as your eyes scan this landscape you detect a certain diversity in the vegetation. This is due largely to the tidal flooding that takes place and the degrees of plant adaptation to this condition. Different plants can withstand different degrees of salinity as do certain animals. What we have then in a tidal marsh is a condition called *degrees of zonation*.

In the low tidal areas of our East coast marshes we find three distinct zones. In the lower tidal zone in the shallow salt water are found killifish, oysters, clams, blue crab, mussels, eelgrass, and sea lettuce. In the mid-tidal zone the salt marsh cordgrass (spartina) appears, along with purple marsh crabs, fiddler crabs, and the cordgrass periwinkle. In the high tide zone are more salt marsh cordgrasses and salt meadow cordgrass. Often just back of the high tide zone shallow depressions or panne appear, and in the pools of salt water left by the high tide one finds such plants as sea lavender, glasswort, spartina, and some algae. Just above the high tide zone in an area of only occasional monthly high floods, are more salt meadow cordgrass, black grass, bayberry, shrubs, and small patches of American holly. Black oak comes in beyond and above the holly.

The clapper rail feeds in the upper two tidal zones as does the king rail, a miscellany of shorebirds, herons, and the pintail duck.

The osprey, laughing gull, and the eagle also find these zones their favorite feeding grounds.

Along the Pacific coast many similar plants are found in the salt marshes although the exact species that are present differ. Moreover, there are only two distinct tidal zones—the cordgrass zone near the water's edge and the dense growth of glasswort in the upper marsh.

The best way to know a salt marsh is to select an area that is convenient and visit it, and the more often you can do it the better.

Several times each spring and sometimes once or twice in the summer I yield to the pleas of a companion and journey with him to the tidal marshes of Matthews County, Virginia. We go by small skiff into the reed country presumably to catch the elusive striped bass or so-called "rockfish" but the real reason for our going is, I suspect, much more than this. Of the many times that we've made these exploits my own total catch of fish has been three rockfish. My partner, Gil, who I admit is a better fisherman, hasn't scored much more. Yet we go. We go because the marsh possesses an attraction all its own.

For those unfamiliar with the Chesapeake Bay marshes there appears little at first to attract the visitor. Just a lot of open wet land, one could say, perhaps a place for an odd boot-clad muskrat trapper or a visiting ornithologist. Or perhaps just a place for a bundled-up waterfowler or two in the winter when the ducks are in. In a general way this is about the size of the human element that ever enters these marshes, and one might say, what a pity! Surely if more people took time out and learned a little about these places, if for nothing more than to bask in the warming sun or just to see the wild things there, we would have more people appreciate these wetlands. If ever there was a place for solitude, for the clearing out of mental cobwebs, the marsh, I believe, is such a place. It is a simple world, off the beaten path, a natural place where a man, no matter how confused, how befuddled, can regain his perspective in quick order and think straight again. The marsh has this kind of quality.

The Chesapeake marshes we visit are big marshes. They stretch

for miles northward and southward encompassing acre upon acre of tidal land. At one point you see only a pine-fringed tree line of the higher shore; at another, only the sparkling blue water. In between is only marsh grass and a water-coursed savannah that stretches to the horizon.

What is the attraction here? Is it solitude? Is it the smoke-free air, or the strange quietness of a wet land when the wind is still? Is it the sounds, the antics of wildlife?

If someone were to ask these questions, I would say that it is perhaps a little of all these things, and more. A marsh is a special biotic community complete in itself with a little of everything thrown in. It is a world so full of living things that one square rod of it can yield enough natural history to fill a book. Perhaps there is a distant ancestral calling here that is both chemical and physiological in aspect and this I would leave to the biochemists to explain.

The most noticeable things in the marsh are, of course, its wild inhabitants. Where Gil and I sojourn and anchor our boat to fish, it's the laughing gulls. We like to see them on sandbars, lifting their black heads skyward, mouths open, squawking in protest as their favorite mud flats get covered by the tide. Their noisy rejoicing from poles and buoys as the tide exposes their favorite sandbar for preening is a delight to see.

Then there are the shrieking cries of the whiteheaded ospreys. They sometimes appear in two's, three's and on occasions in as many as six at a time, fluttering over the marsh, calling, bent on locating a floating fish in the moving tidal channels. Our marsh is true osprey land and these interesting fish hawks can nearly always be seen doing a multitude of things, from snatching tidbits from the tide to building a nest of sticks on an old mud shack in the marsh.

There is special interest, too, in the big brother of the osprey, the bald eagle, as he on rarer occasions puts on a spectacular aerial performance, robbing the fish hawk of its prey. Though not as common a resident of the marsh as the osprey, the lumbering eagle—the most regal bird in America—adds a majestic touch to the scene. Surely he

ings and dessication. It is an environment with many threats, where the threat of being dried to death by the sun is equalled by the threat of being drowned by the sea and where all living is timed to the tides.

One might quickly admit that to the casual visitor this world of the *Littorina* may seem less than great excitement, for nothing is hurried in its life. But the casual look can be misleading. The redwings, rails, and sanderlings know better. So does the clapper rail who looks to the snail for its food. All have stayed long enough to find the marsh a good place to live. Yet for *Littorina* it is a difficult world for here for every predator that comes by land another as deadly steals in from the sea, where subterranean enemies prowl by night and aerial hunters hover by day, and where constantly the most delicate of animal structures must somehow match the rigors of the elements or give in to them and die.

Into this kind of halfway world of special adaptation the lowly periwinkle marsh snail has moved to make its precarious home. Once abundant along the Gulf of Mexico, its kind has moved steadily northward until now the Chesapeake marshes and the Virginia Eastern Shore country have become its ideal home. The choicest habitat of *Littorina* is the open seaside savannah country marked by the salt marsh flats nearest the open sea. So the best periwinkle land is the eastern shore land—a vast 200 square mile area of spartina marshes, a breeding habitat so favorable that all the wet country literally "blooms with periwinkles." From Chincoteague to Fisherman's Island, from Wachapreague to Cedar Island and Parramore, *Littorina* blacken the marsh grass country. So thick are the marine dwellers in this area at times that a man cannot set foot into the spartina without crushing a mass of them into the mud. On Cobb Island, north of the village of Oyster, I have counted as many as 200 *Littorina* in one single square yard of salt marsh.

Natives in the Chesapeake and Shore marsh country refer to the *Littorina* snail simply as "periwinkle," the name presumed to be modified from "petty winkle," the small one, to distinguish it from its larger cousin, the winkle or whelk. In London and some of the Mediterranean cities sea snails are looked upon as a great delicacy. In Holland, Denmark, and Britain, the smaller periwinkles are boiled or steamed and the fleshy parts picked out with a pin and eaten.

Though about 150 species of periwinkles are known to favor the wet zone habitat, it is *Littorina irrorata,* the lined or marsh periwinkle, that has found the environment particularly ideal. Today its numbers are still spreading, known now as far north as New Jersey and beyond. Where its range will end, only the snail itself can tell.

The periwinkle snail, by man's standards, is a most unhurried creature. One afternoon on Wreck Island in Virginia's Northampton County, I sat anchored in a skiff in a salt marsh and watched a *Littorina* snail for two hours. It moved less than a sixteenth of an inch on a blade of spartina. My guide thought that was "awful draggy." He couldn't take it any longer and we pushed ourselves out of that marsh.

Littorina lives for the tide. Encased in its inch-long shell of hard calcium, it dwells in is gloomy subconsciousness between successive inundations and dehydrations, sifting and scraping out the goodness from the plankton, particularly algae, washed to its door by the twice-daily bathings of the tides. Then it seals itself tightly against dry air, like a rubber jar top, as the water ebbs back to the sea. It is a monotonus existence but it is the only life *Littorina* knows and it is a life that has proven safe and good for generations dating back to geologic time.

Death to *Littorina* is certain below the tide line. There, the bitter brine is suffocating. Death is also sure above the wet zone, for the snail needs moisture for its existence. Sunshine and dry air can also be lethal. So *Littorina* clings to its mother grass, the wet spartina, content to spend its time in rhythmic feedings between the tides, followed by long periods of waiting and slumber and occasional imperceptible movement up and down some twelve inches of marsh grass which forms its warm weather home.

Like other marine mollusks of the world, numbering some 80,000 forms, the half to three-quarter inch periwinkle is moved by temperature. When the warm rays of the spring sun penetrate its calciferous outer body, the urge to move and feed and procreate is strong.

Certain specially-adapted structures come into play. Out of the shell orifice comes the soft snail body to begin a period of exploration and slimy movement. When fully extended, the foot becomes as long as the conical shell itself and is capable of exerting prodigious strength. As the snail makes its way over the spartina or mud surface, a mucous layer is laid down over its path. Thus *Littorina* is smart enough to provide its own slippery sliding trail.

It is at night and on dark days following the wash of the tides that the snail most often pushes out its cold fleshy foot, extrudes its stalked, unseeing eyes and somehow led by a dull scent-awareness of its feelers, sets forth on its sojourn of exploration. Breathing is by means of rudimentary gills obtaining oxygen from sea water, into which waste gases are dissolved.

From the delicate mucid flesh of the head, tiny structures project which help the snail to distinguish between light and darkness. Two slender peduncles or stems project out of the head, like antennae of a moth, each tip of which terminates in a half-seeing eye. Close by are two other tentacles, shorter structures, sensory organs by which the snail is able to locate its food by means of scent. The mouth is on the underside of the flesh foot, near the front, and takes the form of a cup-like disc in which is hidden a powerful radula or rasping tongue. With this organ the snail is able to rasp off particles of vegetative food from plants or sessile marine animals. The radula is highly specialized in that it is equipped with hundreds of backward-pointing tiny teeth which, in some snail forms, are capable of penetrating the hardest kinds of shells. A close relative of the periwinkle uses this radula to bore holes into oysters and feed on the flesh, killing them.

Littorina is a hermaphrodite, having both sperm cells and eggs, but it is not capable of self-fertilization. Like other snails it couples with others of its kind, goes through the regular process of mating and fertilization, and gives rise to a cluster of seed-like eggs which before cold weather soon turn into a new generation of tiny periwinkles. These millions of snails enter the food chain in the marsh, being fed upon by fish, birds, and even some mammals.

In the autumn when the winds stiffen and the temperature drops to a new cold, the already slow, inactive *Littorina* feels the urge of long slumber. Quietly and obscurely as it has mated, it slowly glides down the stalk of spartina in search of a resting place. Sometimes it moves all the way down to the mud and there with others of its kind finds a shallow shelter and goes to rest. As the cold increases in the marshes, the sluggish snail sinks deeper and deeper into physical torpor, circulation slowed to nothingness, its faint body awareness weaker and weaker until life itself seems at an end. When excessive cold finally forces the epiphragm to close the shell entrance, *Littorina's* life is lost to the world. It may be a final closing, ending in death, as often happens. Perhaps it is only an act of hibernation, a half sleep, a semi-wakefulness, the process of sleeping of all snails to be followed again in the spring by a rude awakening, by the callings of hunger and movement and procreation; by the urge to live more fully in the marsh again.

Such is the life and destiny of *Littorina* of the salt marsh, the periwinkle snail. It is a life of sleeping, breathing, feeding, of moving about on its muscular foot on the mud surface or on blades of waving spartina, of begetting other generations of periwinkles, of silent crawling and timeless waiting—waiting for the provident washing tide, the plankton and the algae, waiting for the end of one life and the beginning of another.

Life in the Freshwater Marsh

For those who cannot visit the salt marshes, there are some freshwater marshes to see. Here the vegetation is different. Instead of salt grasses and reeds, one notices sedges and cattails. Animal life, too, is different, with muskrats very much at home, their small dome-like houses protruding here and there over the bulrushes.

The late Paul Errington of Iowa, perhaps the country's most noted wildlife biologist on freshwater marshes, found these environments exceedingly fascinating and spent the better part of a lifetime studying them. It is to Dr. Errington that the world owes much for focusing attention on the vital importance of marshes to our total natural environment. It was the love of the muskrat, about which Dr. Errington wrote extensively, that brought this scientist to study the marshes. In like manner, the muskrat has drawn thousands of other men to the marshes —trappers—in quest of the fabulous "brown gold" of America's wetlands.

Life in freshwater marshes can be viewed through several species of marsh residents. One can see the marsh through the redwinged blackbird. But this bird is a migrant and does not stay in the same marsh all year round. The same can be said for certain rails, ducks and geese, and the wading birds. Freshwater marshes are important to all these wildlife forms but as temporary residents, only part of the marsh year is known to them. It remains, therefore, for some other creature to tell us what the freshwater marsh is like the year round. The most typical, most representative of such creatures, is the muskrat.

Known earlier in this country as *muskquash,* the muskrat gets its name from a pair of perineal glands located near the base of the hind legs which release a strong but not too unpleasant musky odor. The fluid was once used in medicines but now has little value. Some trappers, however, collect the musk sacs and bottle them up for scent and use it to lure other muskrats to their traps.

In America the muskrat of the freshwater marshes is widely distributed, ranging from the Arctic Circle to Florida and Mexico. Although a true rodent, the muskrat is better adapted to live in water than on land. Some mammalogists divide the muskrat family into as many as 14 groups or species, but these are quite similar, varying only in color and size.

Probably the most fascinating thing about muskrats, other than the glamour their fur lends to women's coats, is the way they live in the marshes and along stream banks. Few are the country people and travelers who have never seen a dome-shaped muskrat house in a cattailed marsh. These structures are built of water plants and serve primarily as winter homes. The muskrat who lives along stream banks, however, prefers to construct galleries in the mud banks along the river and only occasionally will build a house.

There are two methods of house construction and to know just how construction is done one should study the separate locations where muskrats live, the stream bank and the marsh.

Along a stream which has high banks there is only one method of construction, a gallery type of house with an entrance under water. The muskrat begins to dig under the water in the bank, driving his four- to six-inch wide tunnel upward until he nears the top. If he runs into roots or discovers that he's near the surface, he cuts a tunnel to one side and there excavates a chamber, a living-room-like place which is soon lined with grasses. Later, on the opposite side of this room, he adds another chamber, usually beneath some rushes or roots and to which he adds an air vent. This then is *Ondatra zibethica*'s stream-side home.

The building of a home—lodge house—in the marshes takes quite a different blueprint. If there are no banks, the muskrat builds a foundation of grass, weeds, and sticks, plastering these with mud. Using this same material, he carries the wall of this house up to a dome until it rises two to three feet above the floor of the marsh. Frequently, when muskrat families are big they pool their efforts and build a grand lodge, sometimes making it four to six feet high. Inside the house there is thorough planning and interior decorating. Chambers are constructed with great uniformity, air vents are carefully planned, rooms are lined with soft warm grasses for sleeping. All this is done above the water line, although meticulous care is taken to insure connecting tunnels to the water. Tunnels make for easy escape when danger threatens and prove a good avenue to water and food.

In cold weather, when the marshes freeze over, the muskrat finds it perfectly safe to go down under the ice in search of roots and stems of aquatic plants. He is particularly fond of sweet flag, lily, bulrush, cattail, and wild parsnip, but will eat clams and mussels when available. When the ice covers the pond he carries his food into the upstairs dining room in the lodge where he can munch on it in leisure and still breathe. Muskrats, while remarkably aquatic in habit, can stay under water only a few minutes and must surface frequently for oxygen, like an otter. In warm weather the muskrat prefers to do his dining outdoors, using one or several spots on firm ground for his eating. He is clean of habit and sanitary about his premises.

I once had a good opportunity to study a live muskrat for two days and was amazed by its almost human-like ways. This muskrat was taken alive from a trap by a game warden and was to be used as evidence in a case against a man caught running an illegal trapline in a marsh. We put him in a cage and offered him carrots, celery, and other vegetables. The following morning we checked up on him and found that he hadn't touched a thing. Dismayed at his hunger strike, the warden and I decided to give him his freedom. Taking the little fellow to a pond we decided to tie him down and get some pictures. As soon as he left the barrel and felt the softness of the marsh and smelled the surrounding rushes, he picked up a cattail root and began chewing on it eagerly. He apparently forgot all sense of discomfort and danger and made no effort to get away. After thoroughly gorging himself on rootstocks, he became aware of his personal appearance and promptly began to wash his face with his paws. Face washed, he sat back on his haunches, and in full view of us, began to comb his fur with his front paws. This continued until he was as slick and shiny as a cat. Then he decided it was time to move on. We removed the string and he took off slowly at first and moved into the water much like a beaver and submerged. He soon came up, looked around, then snaked on across the pond on an exploration trip, apparently none the worse for his strange experience.

One week later the warden caught the poaching culprit on the trapline and he was heavily fined for trespassing on another man's property. Our furred friend, meanwhile, was probably well on his way to starting a new colony of muskrats.

The muskrat is by nature a traveler. In late summer, moved by the instinct to procreate, he develops a terrific wanderlust and begins moving about frequently, sometimes great distances. He may go one place for awhile, build a burrow or mound, then leave it half finished to go elsewhere. He may repeat this process until he finds just what he wants, then decides to settle down for the winter. Families run big. Often there are from three to five litters born a year to a pair of muskrats, with an average of six to eight per litter. Usually the first litter is born in April, followed by a second in June or July, and possibly a third in August or September. This is average. The number of litters increases in the south, due to the longer season.

During the summer and early fall the young muskrats remain with their parents with contentment although not exactly under their protection. In spite of the heavy birth rate, muskrats are just holding their own where the trapping isn't too heavy. Shot and trapped heavily on the continent, countless numbers are also destroyed by owls and hawks. The young in the nest are particularly vulnerable to raccoons. In sections of the country where the wild mink is particularly common, this predator gets its full share of young and old muskrats. That a mink will attack a full grown muskrat cannot be disputed. Many trappers have seen these two aquatic creatures in combat, with the muskrat invariably losing out to the mink.

I once watched a mink and a muskrat battle it out in a pond. I was a student at the University of Michigan at the time, majoring in wildlife management, and was running a study strip on furbearers on a farm in Washtenaw County. From signs and tracks I could tell that muskrats and mink were using the same area and, one day unexpectedly, I saw where the two met face to face. I was following a creek to a larger stream when suddenly some commotion in a bend in the river stopped me short. Dropping to a crouch I eased up on the scene of the disturbance and witnessed an amazing spectacle. A big brown mink fully two feet long, had a death grip on a muskrat. He was holding the 'rat by the throat while the spunky muskrat struggled furiously to get loose. The mink kept up the attack until blood began to trickle from the mink's nose. The two tumbled around and around on the sandy bank until the muskrat, breathless and with energy spent, gave up the struggle.

A wild mink is nobody's fool. Alert, always on the move, perpetually hungry like most members of the weasel tribe, it travels long distances, especially at night. It frequents marshes and other wetlands, although I once saw a very large mink deep in the Maine woods far away from water.

The muskrat shares the marsh with many creatures besides the mink and the raccoon. The marsh hawk is a common visitor and is after mice, small muskrats, and snakes. The osprey is also around although he is after mostly fish and frogs.

Perhaps the most noticeable inhabitants of the fresh water marsh are the migrating birds. In some places, like the extensive Bear River Marshes in Utah, the variety and number of migrating waterbirds is hard to believe.

The Bear River Migratory Bird Refuge is essentially a huge marsh. It is located about 15 miles west of Brigham City, Utah, on the delta of the Bear River where it empties into Great Salt Lake. Containing about 65,000 acres, it was established by a special act of Congress on April 23, 1928. It is administered by the Bureau of Sport Fisheries and Wildlife in the Department of the Interior, as an outstanding nesting area and a resting and feeding refuge for waterfowl and other birds that nest in Canada and Alaska and winter southward into Mexico. This is one of the few remaining marshlands where ducks and geese nest in great numbers, and fall concentrations occur in flocks that resemble the descriptions by early explorers.

Migrant waterfowl move into the Bear River marshes beginning in August. By the end of the month, or in early September, the refuge is host to a million waterfowl. Included in this gathering is one of the largest concentrations of whistling swans to be found in the United States; flocks totaling 20,000 frequently are seen by mid-November. Thousands of Canada and snow geese visit the refuge during migration. Predominating in the fall flights are pintails, whose numbers often exceed half a million birds. The green-winged teal is nearly as abundant. As many as 100,000 canvasbacks have visited the refuge at one time during fall migration.

Many of these birds remain into the early winter, leaving the refuge only as cold weather freezes over the water areas. Upon leaving

Bear River, about half of the birds migrate west into California, some move south to Arizona and New Mexico, while others move eastward into Colorado, Texas, and Mexico. With the Spring they return, but the concentrations of birds are smaller, and their stay is shorter. Courtship activities are often seen among the migrants, and the nesting of some species, particularly the Canada goose, begins early.

In the development of this marsh, a system of shallow water impoundments was constructed to conserve and prevent fresh water from entering Great Salt Lake. A roadway on top of the dike around one of these impoundments is open for auto traffic except during the winter. This is a trip of 12 miles and permits observations in one of the best parts of the refuge. Species more or less perculiar to the West and to this area, such as the western grebe, yellow-headed blackbird, avocet, black-necked stilt, long-billed curlew, Wilson's phalarope, white-faced ibis, Franklin's gull, ruddy duck, cinnamon teal, and gadwall may be seen.

The Bear River Marshes also contain a vast network of state-developed marshlands—approximating another 100,000 acres of fresh water marsh country. Thus Utah has in this one great wildlife mecca of federal and state marshes over 165,000 acres of remarkable land.

Birds from these fresh water marshes trade back and forth between various ponds and sloughs and between these fresh water marsh areas and Great Salt Lake itself. One day on Great Salt Lake, a Utah fish and game biologist and I witnessed a spectacle of birds of Great Salt Lake such as I never expected to see. Near an area where Great Salt Lake was receiving a stream of fresh water, small prawn had populated the water and great stretches of shorebirds were after them. They were all Wilson's and northern phalarope. They stretched across the lake bed for a great distance. We estimated their number to be 300,000.

The main duck foods in the fresh water marshes are duckweed and sago pondweed. But these are by no means all. Hundreds of other plants live in the marsh in delicate balance with the animal life. The secret in abundant food production is proper water-level management. Biologists now know just how to manipulate these water levels for maximum plant production. It is, after all, the plants which form the basic item in the food chain of the marsh.

In the late summer and well into September and, even early into October when the wild rice shows its seedy tassel among the cattails, flights of sora descent upon the marshes during the night. They soon fatten up, stay awhile, then leave again for parts further South. The sora is a small rail about the size of a killdeer and is hunted in some places in the autumn.

Seldom do I enter these kinds of marshes in the summertime and not hear one of the oddest and strangest sounds in the animal kingdom. It is the broken base violin string *oonq-la-oonq-la-oonq* of the American bittern. Hard to see in the deep grass country except as a stationary stick-like object in feathers, beak pointing motionless toward the sky, it is one of America's most interesting waterbirds. With him occasionally are seen the snowy egret, common egret, great blue heron, little blue heron, green heron, and the Louisiana heron. All are true marsh birds.

And not to be overlooked in the marsh are the songbirds, amphibians, reptiles and insects. The procession is endless, new, always exciting and captivating for those who are willing to explore and listen.

Many of our fresh water marshes have been lost forever. Those that remain are still isolated, still largely unspoiled for man and creature alike. They are a half world between green water and brown treeless land, where fish and birds and mammals and plants live in harmony and great interdependence, where anyone may see them, as God intended them to be seen, if he but makes a little effort. Here in the seemingly silent, lifeless world of the fresh water marshes, life is so richly rewarding that it pales into insignificance other familiar land areas of the earth. But they, like salt marshes, are disappearing fast. Perhaps if we could know them better, there might be more hope for their preservation.

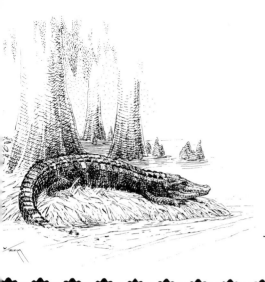

SWAMPS -
ENCHANTING
ENVIRONMENTS

THE DAY WAS ALMOST TOO WARM FOR THE SOJOURNING INDIAN. THE heavy heat and the sun's glare soon had his energy spent and he longed for a rest. He glided his canoe into the shade of a baldcypress and halted. The aroma of sweet-smelling honeysuckle was delectably strong and he took in deep breaths of it. He had come to the swamp where his ancestors had captured Captain John Smith and a long strenuous morning of paddling around submerged trees, stumps and blowdowns had him weary. He wedged the canoe in the crevice of a heavy-buttressed tree, slid back in the seat and stretched out. Overhead his dark eyes caught the appearance of white pillows of clouds as they floated leisurely across the heavens, like puffs of streaming smoke, and his ears caught the lapping of water against the canoe. Soon the Chickahominy redskin was sound asleep.

Suddenly, not fifty feet away, a loud *keer-YANK, KRANK, KRANK* blasted the swamp as a bird with awkward wings struggled into the air. As he passed overhead he uttered several more shrieks for good measure and disappeared. For a moment in his partial wakefuless, the Indian was back to the steaming Jurassic and the great blue heron might easily have been a Pterosaurus flying by.

Great swamps are like that. The native or the visitor never really knows what will break the calmness of a noonday hour. One minute it might be the shrieks of birds, the next the "pop" of feeding fish, the third minute the splash of turtles gliding from a floating log. And sometimes it may be nothing more than the simple creaking of a big snag in the watery timber. All are part of the eternal symphony of that wet wilderness with the forbidding name, *swamp*.

But swamps are enchanting worlds. They are not fetid, as some would think, nor do they possess quicksands ready to engulf men and beasts. But they do have a mood and air of mystery about them which makes them, to a naturalist at least, enticing and irresistible. And few places on earth, acre for acre, can match the swamp in rare and unique forms of plants and animals. A swamp, in simple terms, is a wet, partially inundated forest area where water stands or flows, quietly, all of the year or part of the time. Ecologically, a swamp is a sort of midway land between a marsh and a bog. The true marsh is a wet, treeless area marked by herbaceous vegetation. A bog, on the other hand, is what most swamps get to be when left alone—usually to become a semi-treeless, low area, with quaking watery surfaces, sphagnum moss, and heavy floating vegetation.

Bogs are common in depressed areas in the northern United States and Canada and are characterized by poor drainage and abundant rainfall. They are important as *natural areas,* and possess immeasurable scientific value.

Swamps and their closely related counterparts, the marshes, are usually formed by natural forces—wind, ice, water or snow. The action of these agents often blocks the escape routes of water and, when wooded areas become inundated more or less permanently, swamps appear. Some swamps can be traced to earthquakes, some to landslides and floods, some to the actions of animals, such as the beaver. And some are traced to man's activities.

In northern states swamps of several types occur. New Jersey has its Great Swamp characterized by watery thickets of willow, alder, red maple, and river birch. Maine has its black spruce swamps, some so impenetrable that even a deer has difficulty passing through them. Northern New York has some of the most outstanding white cedar swamps in North America. Michigan, Wisconsin, Minnesota have swamps which are a mixture of spruce, fir and white cedar—all important wintering grounds of the white-tailed deer.

Bogs are found where swamp trees die out because of excessive water, acidity, and oxidation. A quaking bog is a thick mattress of living and decomposed vegetation which literally floats over standing water. A man can stand in the midst of such bogs and poke long poles through them to test the depth of water below. In the Adirondacks, I once pushed a ten-foot pole through a bog mattress over water and it went out of sight. The bottoms of most bogs are laden with mud and ooze but the final base is one of solid clay.

The interesting thing about bogs is that they often are the homes of rare wild plants, like the Venus flytrap and the pitcher plant, both of which are classed as insectivorous plants. These plants are so uniquely constructed that they actually trap and devour insects. However, the captured animals do not form the essential foods of these plants. The remains of such creatures are simply absorbed into the water systems of the plants, while their main foods still must be produced by photosynthesis.

Bogs by and large are mere vestiges or remnants of persistent nature which date back to Pleistocene times. The glaciers, which swept over the swamplands of upper North America during the last million years, did not do a clean job of it and often left pockets of original lowland after them. In other areas they left bogs far below the advance of the ice fields.

One such bog is the Cranesville Swamp in West Virginia. Located in rugged country, at the 2500-foot elevation, this small 250-acre relict bog is a living museum of bygone eras.

The University of West Virginia had purchased Cranesville from The Nature Conservancy and was wondering how best to use it. The Nature Center Planning Division of the National Audubon Society was called in to make a survey and protection plan. When the report finally came out a few months later, a strong endorsement was made for the

University to safeguard the area as a "rare and priceless area, a nature-realm of great ecological and scientific value worthy of the highest kind of protection."

The bog had low temperature pockets caused by warm air moving upward and the surrounding cold mountain currents coming into the area and persisting. Hence the tops of the hemlocks, which cannot withstand excessively low temperatures, freeze easily and make a special kind of a burned-looking area.

Bogs, such as Cranesville are literally living museums. Their value is of the same sort as a museum only they preserve specimens of the living world itself. Scientific research in many fields of biology, including such fields as bio-ecology and taxonomy, are dependent on such areas. Even the laboratory branches of biology, such as physiology and genetics, find natural areas of considerable value. Scientists need such places as check areas in land-use to gauge the effects of farming, forestry, and other land uses. These areas also serve as sanctuaries for rare species that might otherwise face extinction.

Most people possess a horrible fear of swamps and have little desire to go roaming around in them. This feeling arises largely out of a total unfamiliarity with them, including horror tales of quagmires and quicksands, all of which make good publicity but none of which can be documented. Our own government did little to brighten the picture when it passed the Land Swamp Act of 1849-50, which gave landowners an incentive to drain such lands for agriculture. But science today is uncovering the real importance of swamplands and is giving us new insights into their role in the total environment. Now at last there is a nationwide movement to save swamplands, including other types of wetlands, before it is too late.

The naturalist roaming around a big swamp cannot help but be reminded of the prehistoric past when these steaming and hot lands trembled under the feet of huge dinosaurs when their awesome quiet was often broken by the terrifying cries of battling reptiles. Certainly no natural world is more closely related to the great carboniferous forests of the Mesozoic Era than the swamps we still see today.

One of the choicest swamps saved for posterity is Corkscrew Swamp, east of Naples, Florida. Credit for this must go to the National Audubon Society and the Florida Audubon Society who together worked hard to save it. Today a convenient boardwalk allows visitors to become intimately acquainted with this remarkable area—a relict baldcypress swamp of fascinating air plants, mosses, ferns, water plants, vines, great trees, and easily observed alligators, water birds and other wildlife.

Perhaps the most historically famous swamp along the Atlantic coast is the Great Dismal Swamp, where George Washington and William Byrd traveled and worked. Once viewed as dark, forbidding and even dismal, the swamp has lost much of its character and charm, yet it still has few equals as a wildlife swampland in America. To be sure, Georgia has its Okefenokee and Florida its Everglades, but there is only one Great Dismal Swamp. There is a distinct quality about it that holds the wayfarer in a spell and, once he is stricken, he keeps returning year after year.

Appropriately named, the swamp sprawls over 750 square miles of dense, partially inundated forest land in southern Virginia and northeastern North Carolina. Sportsmen call it a veritable outdoor wonderland. And game biologists point out that as a wildlife area few stretches of wild land in the east offer greater potential for scientific investigation and wildlife development. Yet the area is doomed, unless concerted efforts are made to save it from further exploitation. Further development and drainage will ruin the swamp unless exploitation is kept out.

The heart of Great Dismal Swamp is Lake Drummond. This coffee-colored, fresh-water lake, usually calm and quiet, which measures about seven miles long by five miles across, is strangely picturesque and round as a perfect jewel. Long shrouded in mystery, hidden deep in legend, the sweet-water lake has been the subject of innumerable stories and weird tales. Of it, wrote the eloquent Irish poet, Thomas Moore:

". . . through tangled juniper, beds and reeds, through many a fen where the serpent feeds, and man never trod before."

Moore's immortal poem, *Lake of the Dismal Swamp,* was scrawled out on a piece of paper in a Main Street tavern in Norfolk, Virginia, following the poet's visit to Lake Drummond in 1803. It characterizes the charm imparted by this region even at that early date. Moore was then a consul to Bermuda and was visiting the Old Dominion as guest of Colonel Hamilton, British consul.

Geologically the great swamp is an elaboration of an immense spring which overflows in all directions. Its maximum elevation in the heart of the swamp is from ten to fifteen feet above sea level and from this point there is a gradual sloping outward and downward of the land. The swamp's heartland was once covered by sea water and a part of the underwater Atlantic continental shelf. Over the ages the region gradually lifted itself out of the sea to form an interesting and unique geologic phenomenon. Along the western margin of the swamp is a well-defined ancient sea beach, the Nansemond escarpment, which rises five to fifty feet to a natural boundary. It is here where George Washington did much of his surveying.

The swamp is said to include the major northeastern extension of the great palustrine forest which in early days dominated the landscape of the Coastal Plain of the United States. Although much of the area has been deforested and burned by wild fires, extensive patches of fine timber still remain. Trees, such as cypress, several gums, and water ash, thrive in dense stands. Botanists and foresters term the swamp a fine outdoor laboratory. Students of natural history find the swamp rich in fauna and flora. Scientists call the swamp a "relict area"—a natural and largely undisturbed plant community.

Wildlife abounds in the Great Dismal Swamp. Black bear and wildcat persist, deer are abundant, mink and otter and bobcat occasionally are seen. Swamp-loving birds are common. Several species of game fish, notably black crappie and a small sunfish, the flier, find the swamp to their liking. The black bass, however, does not thrive because the water is too acid.

My first acquaintance with the swamp came through a Virginia game warden, Sheldon Roundtree, who knew the swamp as well as anyone. He took me there one spring day when the honeysuckle perfumed the countryside. We drove to Wallaceton from Suffolk, put in at an improvised boat landing on the Dismal Swamp Canal, and went buzzing along in our 14-foot outboard up the Feeder Ditch to the government locks. Here the boat had to be winched over some 50 yards of land and put into the final portion of the Feeder Ditch canal leading to Lake Drummond.

When we roared out of the ditch and saw Lake Drummond, I was overwhelmed. Shivers ran all through me. It was like some masterpiece on canvas. Never had I seen a lovelier lake in such a wild semi-tropical setting. Indeed it looked every inch a lake out of the prehistoric past.

Because the Great Dismal Swamp is unique, the establishment of a national forest or park has long been advised. However support for such a move has never been forthcoming from the state or the federal agencies. Groups, such as the Norfolk Association of Commerce, the Norfolk Chapter of the Izaak Walton League of America, and other organizations, have long recommended a park but, somehow, sadly, the momentum for such a project has never gotten off the ground. So the threat of exploitation continues.

Perhaps the most intriguing swamp in America is Okefenokee. One can read about this place many times but only seeing it firsthand will reveal its true pristine beauty.

Okefenokee is, indeed, a watery world of outstanding quality. Lying in southeastern Georgia near the Florida state line, it is one of the largest, oldest, and most primitive swamps in America. Much of the area is a federal wildlife refuge which extends some 38 miles from north to south and 25 miles across at its widest part. The refuge alone totals 329,000 acres.

Okefenokee is really a big bog—a vast dying swamp with unique geologic and paleontological history. This geological oddity was once a mud-cup in the ocean's floor, a product of an ancient sea, like Great Dismal Swamp, but over the epochs it rose out of the ocean until today it is a hundred feet above sea level. The swamp is an inviolate haven for bear, deer, raccoon, bobcat, otter, alligator, and many aquatic birds. Much of it is an indescribable botanical garden—a watery wilderness of mosses, lichens, wildflowers, sedges, shrubs, and trees. Some plants

are so rare that they have only recently been identified by botanists.

Distinctive in all seasons of the year, the "land of trembling earth" —as the swamp is known to the Seminole Indians—is particularly fascinating in the spring. April days and nights are particularly rewarding.

One can stand transfixed in the night as a swampland orchestra unfolds its musical arrangement. An owl sounds his distant call in the woods. You know from its voice that it is a Florida barred owl. It is sometimes referred to locally as the eight-hooter because its call sounds like, *"Who cooks for you . . . who cooks for you? . . . who cooks?"* Some area residents say this isn't quite right, that it sounds more like, *"I cook for you, I cook for you!"*

In the evening, U.S. Fish and Wildlife Service agents go out on their night patrols for 'gator hunters. With alligators on the increase in the protected refuge—the population estimates range from 5,000 to 10,000 and with hides selling for five to six dollars a foot—poaching has become a lucrative business. These patrolmen go out risking their lives to try to stop it.

The Okefenokee has two distinct habitats. One is a watery world of cypresses with tangled bay and gum trees, Spanish moss, ponds and lakes, and narrow river courses. This is the watery woodland habitat and occupies almost the entire western portion of the swamp. It is more open, often called prairie or glades country, and is a region largely of shallow water with lily pads, iris, arrowhead, and floating muck. In places the muck is so thick and heavy that a bird or mammal can walk on it. In later stages these areas form floating islands. Beneath the matted material are several feet of muck water and heavy ooze. The mucky material rises to the surface as a result of gaseous action resulting from decaying vegetation at the bottom. When the mats get large and begin to sprout herbaceous vegetation, the local natives call them "mounds." When the vegetation gets more advanced, they are called "houses." When these get to support tree life, they are called "hammocks."

The alligator is the swamp's most primitive and interesting denizen. The female reptile lays from 50-60 eggs and the young, although protected for a while by the mother, are exceedingly vulnerable to turtles, raccoons, and large wading birds. To see an alligator in the wild takes good eyesight and to approach one requires stealthy boat craftsmanship. One day on a visit to the swamp, our guide, Lenard Walker, a young, quiet and soft-spoken biologist, was determined to show my companion, Byron Ashbaugh, and me some alligators. He was on hand in the morning with his flat-bottomed skiff and motor, ready to take us over the lakes and water trails of the western section. "We have four hours," he said, "just let me know when you want to stop or take pictures. We may see a 'gator and when we do, better be ready. They don't stay for long."

After several hours of weaving and dodging and jockeying along cypress-draped water trails, cruising over mirrored ponds and lakes, including Billy's Lake, Len cut his motor and pointed.

It was an alligator all right and a big one. He was sunning himself on a mound of muck and lay fully exposed in the sunlight. We glided within eighty feet of him, snapping pictures when, suddenly, he jet-propelled into the lake like a rocket, splashing water high on all sides. In an instant we spotted him far up ahead of us making a big wake as he headed for another sunny spot. This fellow was about eleven feet long and showed much more life than one would imagine when seeing the sluggish creature at rest.

An extraordinary amount of misinformation exists about alligators, mostly about their size and ferocity. Actually American alligators, while growing large, seldom reach anything like what the stories say. A ten-footer is a good-sized 'gator. An eleven-footer is a real big one and a twelve- or thirteen-footer is a giant. There have been records of fourteen-foot alligators, but sixteen- and eighteen-footers grow only in people's imagination. Also, alligators never attack people. There has never been an authentic case on record where an alligator, unprovoked, attacked a human being. Their favorite foods are the slower-moving reptiles, snakes and turtles, and wounded or unsuspecting fish, birds and mammals.

These reptiles enjoy sunning themselves during the day and often crawl onto mounds or logs and wait for prey. Sometimes they lie submerged with only their heads out of water—seemingly dozing but subconsciously alert. However, an alligator in an "alley" or "draw" is to be respected. When approached from behind he will suddenly turn violently and make for open water, and this can be dangerous. His tail is muscular and powerful and can do great damage to a boat or a man if either gets into the path of his escape.

Late that morning, Len had shown us several 'gators but we could approach none very closely. Always they would plunge into the water or merely sink. Finally, Byron spotted one with only his two-foot head showing out of water. Len cut the motor and we glided toward him, Byron in the bow of the boat, camera ready, I in the middle with my Speed Graphic.

Slowly we eased within fifteen feet of this fellow until I could see the redness of his eye. Motionless and seemingly asleep, the 'gator stood his ground. Closer and closer we came, Byron fearlessly shooting pictures one right after another. In another second we were within ten feet of his head, then nine, then eight. Now things rose to a climax quickly. At five feet it was eyeball to eyeball for Byron and the 'gator. Still the 'gator held steady. At that moment a boatload of fishermen came down the lake and saw us and one man yelled, "Watch out. He's the meanest one in the swamp."

Suddenly the big reptile started to swell. Len reached for a paddle. I grabbed an oar. Now it was only four feet to the 'gator's head. As he pulled in air his full body rose to the surface, like a submarine, exposing his horny incredible length, tail now commencing to lash back and forth, a defiant, angry bull alligator. At this split instant he expelled a loud, furious hiss and leaped forward with a roar, splashing water all over us. He was gone in a second. All of us sighed. Had he chosen to come across our boat, I believe we would have been in for some trouble. It was an episode we'll always remember.

This western section of Okefenokee has some sixty lakes and ponds and alligators are quite common. On spring mornings you can hear the bulls bellowing—a distant rumbling sound like logs falling off a truck. We heard the roar several times but did not see any of the beasts actually sounding off.

Majestic moss-draped cypresses and gnarled black gum trees predominate in this forested portion, providing a somber background for the delicate beauty and sweet fragrance of the blooming white bay and cassena, while "hurrah bush" and "bamboo brier" form a dense tangled, often impenetrable, undergrowth of vegetation. Most of the open surface water along the edges is covered with arrowhead, pickerel weed and a spade-like plant called, never-wet.

The "prairies" of this section occupy roughly 15 per cent of the swamp and are shallow flooded marsh areas which sustain a colorful mixture of white and yellow waterlily, never-wet, pickerel weed, paint root, hardhead, beakrush, and maidencane. Scattered throughout the prairies are various-sized islets supporting shrubs, willow, gum and bay. In the more treeless areas there are small prairie lakes, 'gator holes, canals, and boat runs. In the open waters of the so-called Suwannee River section are found Billy's Lake, Minnie's Lake and Bib Water. It is here where the rich variety of the swamp's fauna and flora is found—a veritable lush, subtropical Garden of Eden.

The uplands bordering the swamp are clothed in longleaf and slash pine. Some spots are dotted with occasional hardwood clumps or "hammocks," interspersed with occasional cypress or black gum.

The swamp's varied habitat—a marvelous mixture of cypress and black gum, of prairies and floating mounds, of open water and pine barrens, of isles and hammocks—affords a haven for large numbers of birds. In the fall, robins by the hundreds of thousands congregate in this area to feed on the bounteous crop of black gum and gallberry fruits. All species of ducks common to the Atlantic flyway find protection in the prairies. The food supply for most puddle ducks, however, is strikingly limited. Apparently, the high acidity of water and other chemical factors prevent the development of choice waterfowl foods. Here, also, the sandhill crane makes its home the year-round and the wild turkey inhabits the pine barrens. Fish-eating birds—the herons, white and wood ibises, anhingas, and kingfishers—are common along the water courses most of the year.

A total of 201 species of birds have been recorded from Okefenokee Swamp by visiting ornithologists and refuge personnel. An additional 22 species, which are of accidental, very rare, or former occurrence, also have been reported. A delightful common spring bird is the prothonotary warbler, the male with delicate blue wings and head and breast of orange-tinted gold, often can be seen darting among the cypresses. They add a flashing, majestic touch to the dark-shrouded water trails as the boat goes gliding by.

For the more casual visitor who finds the federal refuge too big an undertaking, there is the small and beautiful private Okefenokee Swamp Park. It, too, is preserving for posterity a portion of the natural wonders of this area. The policies of the park are aimed at services to visitors but they adhere to strict conservation practices. Hunting and trapping are forbidden in keeping with those generally adopted by the U.S. Fish and Wildlife Service. But fishing is permitted with approved guides.

The park is administered as a non-profit development operating under long-term lease. Thus the awesome and mysterious swampland is made accessible to the general public, permitting visitors to see and enjoy a "forbidden world" where for many generations only stout-hearted adventurers, trappers, hunters and lumbermen dared to tread. Okefenokee Swamp Park has designed its facilities and its program to answer the yearning of the mildly adventurous who wish to penetrate into part of the recesses of the swamp and yet do so in reasonable comfort.

The vistor will enjoy an hour, or a day, or even a succession of days in this area. He can enjoy the incomparable charm of a lost world; see unforgettable pristine beauty, climb a high tower in the swamp with a commanding and breathtaking view, and be a witness to the unfolding of a weird watery wilderness that dates back to the predawn of man's history.

The Okefenokee Swamp is being heralded to the visiting world in motion pictures, magazines and newspapers, television, radio, comic strips, by writers of historical and documentary books, and fiction, by lecturers, naturalists and educators. Yet, only a personal visit to this "Land of Trembling Earth," can truly reveal its romantic and mysterious charm. One can capture the spirit of Okefenokee only by seeing it.

THE EVERGLADES–
RIVER OF GRASS

SOUTHWARD FROM LAKE OKEECHOBEE, BETWEEN INDIAN PRAIRIE AND Big Cypress Swamp on the west and the rocky seaside ridge of Florida's east coast, sprawls a savannah of nature unique in America. It is found only in one area, in subtropical and tropical southeastern United States, and it is as strikingly special as it is, in fact, nationally famous. This is the Everglades—the wondrous country of the "river of grass."

The region of the river of grass spreads southward in an ever-widening and somewhat curving basin until its fresh waters merge with those of salt in the south in a labyrinth of sloughs and creeks and inlets called the Ten Thousand Islands.

Although TV shows, travelogues, and brochures have created immense interest in this primitive landscape and the disappearing alligator and the water shortage in the Everglades have aroused national concern, the true "river of grass" remains little known.

Almost all newcomers to Florida think that the Everglades is confined within the boundaries of Everglades National Park, and that, if they stroll along the trails and the boardwalks provided by the park, they have "seen the Everglades." However, only ten percent of the Everglades is situated in the national park. Forty-one percent of the region is privately owned.

The remaining forty-nine percent of the sawgrass-covered land is within the jurisdiction of the Central and Southern Florida Flood-Control District. These 1,345 square miles of wilderness are used as water-storage areas, but the district has also opened the acreage to fishing, hunting, shell-collecting, and bird-watching.

For two generations the white man was content to skirt the edges of what he regarded as the forbidding Everglades and he seldom ventured therein. Then came the first big real estate grab and an attempt to exterminate the Seminole or remove him from his land. A campaign that was bitterly resisted by the great Indian Chief, Osceola. There were further remarkable developments after the Indians were crushed.

The Everglades have, or should we say once had, several floristic features. Their edges are fringed by such natural plant-associations as flatwoods, pinelands, small prairies, or "glades," and hammocks. The later plant-association, truly a jungle, although really a minor element in the structure of the Everglade vegetation, gave to the general public through superficial observation, the erroneous idea of the Everglades. Aboriginal mounds or ruins of aboriginal occupation and civilization are also to be met with on the outskirts and in the interior.

To one who has been through the Everglades, several major elements in its superficial geology and vegetation are evident. At the upper end there is a shallow basin which, always filled with water, constitutes Lake Okeechobee. As the aborigines sometimes termed it Mayami, it appears as Lake Mayami on some of the early maps of Florida.

Up to a few years ago, on the rim of Lake Okeechobee, particularly on the eastern side, a primeval forest-hammock developed. Here, cypress trees and various broadleaved temperate-region trees, such as the maple, the ash and the elm, and a few tropical trees formed a plant-association of indescribable beauty. On the southern side between the open waters of the lake and the Everglade prairie there had accumulated an enormous deposit of humus unequaled by a similar structure in the United States. This accumulation of humus, essentially a gigantic sponge, covering thousands of acres varying from one foot to several feet in depth, supported an association of pond-apple and elder unique in all of North America. The Everglades south of Lake Okeechobee, for half the distance to the Bay of Florida, are merely saw-grass prairie, with just the same amount of relief as mid-ocean in calm weather. In the more southern portion the surface is dotted by myriad hammock islands ranging from a small fraction of an acre to several acres in extent.

When I first saw the Everglades they were wild and superbly exciting. Now, some forty years later, much of the area has changed. Some of it for the better because now in part of the region there is a national park, yet much of it for the worse because of drainage and development.

The river of grass is neither true marsh nor true swamp, but a sixty-mile-wide prairie of moving fresh water. It has open herbaceous land areas and closed islands of trees. In one sense, the region is a strange delicate mixture of uniqueness and wild tranquility.

Early in the 1900s, the Florida Federation of Women's Clubs, aided by farsighted garden clubs, saw the value of preserving some of the "river of grass" country and decided to do something about it. They decided to establish a lonely glade hammock, Paradise Key, as the first truly tropical natural park in America—Royal Palm State Park. Some twenty years later the Congress, sensing the deep national significance of this small park as well as another three million acres surrounding it, created the Everglades National Park.

The park was to remain forever a natural and pristine area—a verdant watery paradise for wildlife. But time changes things. Today the Everglades Park and the Everglades outside the park have been changed drastically.

When I worked as a young park naturalist on Paradise Key, the small state park was a tropical gem in the vast wilderness of sawgrass, hammocks, palmettos, mangroves, pondcypress, sloughs, ponds, and grassy lakes. On a few lush islands majestic royal palms towered over the landscape. Colorful tree snails were present by the thousands. The blue sky went white with flocks of ibises. Wood storks bent the mangrove tree limbs to the ground. Paradise Key lived up to its name.

A. E. Livingston, a quiet but well known local surveyor and a man under whom I gained much training in natural history, said once that the Everglades were the "last of a Pleistocene epoch passing before our eyes." I believed him, and now I believe even more what he said—that man will pose a serious threat to the park as well as what remains of the Everglades outside the park. The big question and bone of contention in the present fight to save the Everglades is water—not just surface water, but an adequate supply of fresh water underground and the prevention of salt water from entering the freshwater aquifers and subterranean porous oolite limestone in the southern portion.

Nowhere is water and wildlife more closely interrelated than in the Everglades. When I worked in the area with the Civilian Conservation Corps, the Everglades was true to its name—it was a river of grass, a river so wide that it took days to cross it. Indeed, some never crossed it! In the winter months, water was everywhere. Waterbirds and alligators and deer and wild turkeys were abundant. Fish, dozens of different kinds, seethed in a sea of grass in the sloughs. In summer months when the rainfall was low, the waters dropped somewhat, but only a few feet or so. There was still plenty of water in the canals and ponds and sloughs for everything that needed it: for the coot, purple

gallinule, the water turkey, ibis, several herons, and the alligator. Everything, including the Seminole Indians followed the waters back and forth, outward from the sloughs with the rains, back again to the sloughs during the droughts, a great glade country with an enormous pulsating heart, a heart that never stopped. Now the heart beat is slowing down—it is dying of thirst.

The Early Days

In the early days those of us in the CCC saw so much wildlife that one could not believe his eyes. Once I came face to face with a cougar at Taylor's Slough. Anhingas and water moccasins were so plentiful that I could show a dozen of them to visitors in a single afternoon. Wood ibis were thick.

One experience was so vivid that I can still feel it. I was leading a small group of northerners over a jungle trail pointing out tree snails and poisonwood and strangler fig when suddenly a strange roar came from over the Everglades. I was new to the country and had never heard such a noise before.

"For heaven's sake, what's that!" inquired one of my startled visitors. "Sounded like diving airplanes of some kind."

"I really don't know," I said, "but we'll be coming to a clearing soon and we'll look."

In a few minutes we came to a bridge with a good view. A small six foot alligator was sunning himself along the water's edge. Several great blue herons flew out of the water, squawking, and a large gang of Florida gallinules paddled away at our approach. I took my binoculars and began scanning the sawgrass plains ahead. Suddenly, I caught a glimpse of something strange in the distance. Far over the distant Everglades a tremendous flock of white birds could be seen. They were climbing slowly upward and upward, into the big blue sky. I pointed them out and passed my glasses around so all could see. Up they spiralled, up into the heavens, a great cloud of glistening white wings. Each speck sparkling like a crystal of ice in the sun. Upward still they went, twisting, shimmering, turning, their pattern changing every minute. I recognized them as white ibises and they must have numbered

THE EVERGLADES—RIVER OF GRASS   123

5,000 birds. Then the huge flock stopped climbing and held poised aloft for a moment—a big white mass of birddom in the sky. They seemed to be about a mile above the ground at this point. Then an incredible thing happened. The leader of the flock suddenly folded his wings and led his great flock of followers into an unbelievable dive toward the earth. Down they came, wings folded tight, the sound of moving air passing between them growing louder and louder—an avalanche of birds plummeting earthward toward the Everglades. Down they roared until at the very moment of contact with the ground they pulled out of it, the maneuver sending a mighty drone across the sawgrass country.

We shook our heads in disbelief and began to breathe again. It was the most stupendous sight and sound from birds I had ever witnessed and it chilled me to the bone. Such a spectacle did not occur often, not even in the Everglades, and when it did it left every onlooker utterly speechless.

The white ibis still flies over the Everglades today but its numbers are down, as are many other forms of wildlife. The lowering of the water table, loss of habitat to agriculture and development, have taken a frightful toll of both wild animals and plants. However, Americans are indeed fortunate to have the Everglades National Park where at least a semblance of a wild tropical area can still be seen. Its establishment however, came none too soon. When I first knew the area in 1933-34 there was only Royal Palm State Park. But it was the nucleus of a conservation move and the Everglades National Park did not come until 1947.

Even in those early days, however, one had to go into the very heart of the Everglades, away from the few roads, away from the trails, to really know and get a feel of the country.

Everglades Safari

A safari I like to remember occurred during my last weeks with the Civilian Conservation Corps. It occurred at the time when I was helping Mr. Livingston run transit lines on Paradise Key. Because of his surveying work he knew the 'glades like no other man and was always good for an adventure.

"Mr. Livingston," I said to him one morning, "why can't we quit this work for a day . . . maybe do something in the open where the mosquitos aren't so bad . . . like making that trip?"

The old man dropped his head, peered over his horn-rimmed glasses, and smiled understandingly. Then as if on purpose he went back to cutting a big liana vine in the trail. With three great whacks of his Spanish machete, he cut through the vine, then slowly walked over to our transit. He lit a cigarette and, taking several deep, long drags, blew streamers of smoke into the wild coffee bushes. "All right, my boy," he said, his mind made up, "we'll go. We'll do it. We'll pack this afternoon and go tomorrow. We'll take George here with us and go to Cape Sable."

I don't remember exactly what I said, but George, my companion guide, claimed later that the announcement hit us like a bombshell from heaven. Cape Sable. We couldn't believe it. This was the last word in adventure. It was like a safari in Africa. For months the trip

was only talk: the fabulous country, the fishing, the treacherous mangroves, inlets filled with barracudas, the colorful birdlife, the majestic Gulf. And for months Mr. Livingston had been promising us a trip. "We'll go someday boys," he'd say, "We'll go." But now we were really going.

One lives hard and restless on an expectant night. When the rosy dawn finally came, the sawgrass plains never looked more beautiful. We were ready, George and I, and our hearts swelled with excitement. Livingston's battered Model A pickup appeared on time and was loaded to the brim. With the dignified, quiet old man at the wheel, we rolled out of Paradise Key over a coral-bedded overgrown road and headed for the desolate country to the southwest. As we jolted over one bad place around a turn, flocks of roseate spoonbills rose from the sloughs and winged away for the more distant hammock flats. There they settled heavily among the myrtle bushes and squawked at us for disturbing them. Now and then Livingston pointed to a large alligator but each time his finger went up the reptile would be away in a splash in the canal.

In those days the 28 miles to Coot Bay and the Gulf of Mexico was a difficult and hard trip. The road was barely passable in places and we stopped often to fill holes in the road or remove fallen snags. Today a new road and a smooth ride brings the visitor to the coast in less than thirty minutes. But considering our circumstances, our progress was good until we hit the mangroves.

Livingston knew the lay of the land well. As chief surveyor in the southern Everglades, he knew every acre of the country, every section like the palm of his hand. As we advanced the going grew rougher and rougher until at times we felt sure our springs would go. But somehow they held and we managed to rattle and swish and creak up to a point where the road just vanished.

"This is as far as we can go," Livingston said with finality. It was an open grove ringed with royal and cabbage palms. "We'll camp here. The Gulf is still south of us, and the Cape another several miles up the beach. You boys game, are you?"

He didn't have to ask. George and I went to work immediately. In minutes our tent was up under a small live oak. Mr. Livingston made a fire and we had a quick lunch of sardines, crackers and hot tea.

We put everything away and powdered ourselves with sulphur to ward off the chiggers. Livingston suggested we travel light. "Might have to swim an inlet or two. So just take your tackle, canteen, camera and binoculars. I'll lead the way with a machete."

With tackle box in one hand and a surf rod in the other I followed Livingston out of the grove, while George trailed behind with the camera equipment. The going was Indian style at first, bobbing and weaving and bending to avoid thorn bushes and briars. Livingston slashed away now and then with his machete as he came upon the worst of the thickets, keeping out a watchful eye at the same time for diamondbacks.

"These brackish flats are favorite hiding places for rattlers," he cautioned. "Can run as big as your leg and twice as long, so keep your eyes open and legs springy." But the big gray reptiles stayed out of our way and we had no trouble. But cottonmouth moccasins were a common sight and we saw dozens of them sunning in the sloughs. But unless one bothered them they posed no problem.

After about an hour of tough going in heavy undergrowth we came to a wet place where the cane and sawgrass parted. Ahead loomed a dazzling bright horizon. We moved out of the dark covered undergrowth and climbed onto a small sand hillock. Ahead of us lay a vast apron of palmettoes interlaced everywhere with masses of red mangroves. It was our last barrier before the Gulf. The day was hot and humid and sweat rolled from us in big wet beads. Livingston pushed on. In a few minutes he topped another small sand dune, stopped and sighed. Four hundred yards ahead sprawled the majestic Gulf of Mexico—a vast, jade green jewel of shimmering water, wide and expanseful and ruffled by a myriad of gentle whitecaps, all stretching out as far as the eye could see. Overhead hung great pillows of cumulus clouds, as if suspended from the hands of some heavenly puppeteer above.

We stood on top of a sand ridge in silence and took in deep breaths. No landscape picture was ever more beautiful; no sun ever more brilliant. Eyes watering profusely, I caught the outline of the ocean shore. For one or two miles the waterline skirted a mass of mangroves, then curved gently inland out of sight, only to reappear again in the distance. On and on it flowed until it terminated in a palm-fringed cape —Cape Sable.

"Well, there you see it, boys," Livingston gasped. "God's land! God's country!" There was a deep feeling in the old man's voice, almost one of reverence, and his dry heavy lips quivered. No longer was he the taciturn man of Paradise Key. Something very profound had moved him.

"Wildest spot in America, boys," he breathed. "Look at that shore . . . those palms. Boys, this is where Ponce de Leon landed 400 years ago, searching for the Fountain of Youth. Not fifty white men have seen this place since; Seminoles yes, but not white men."

When Livingston finally quieted down and smoked a cigarette, we gathered our senses together and pushed on. But visible excitement gathered within us at every step. When we finally gained the actual water's edge and the beach we felt like children and raced out wildly into the shallow surf, clothes and all. So exhilarating, so delightful was the water that for a moment we forgot all about the trek yet to be made to Cape Sable.

After we had bathed for several minutes to the noisy protests of gulls and terns, and not a few disturbed pelicans, we picked up our gear and resumed the journey. The sojourn along the beach proved to be one distraction after another: thousands of shells, great quantities of driftwood, masses of seaweed, loose coconuts, turtle eggs. Livingston kept urging us on. What a paradise for a beachcomber, I thought, and hurried on. Livingston kept leading the way, scattering flocks of sandpipers and other shorebirds from the beach as we advanced. Overhead more flocks of gulls careened and squawked. Now and then a bird would dive down to the surf, snatch a floating morsel, flap back into the air and ride out the breeze like a kite in the sky.

Halfway to the Cape we came across a deep inlet where a stream carried chalky-colored water to the sea. There was no choice. We had to swim it. I was reluctant to do so at first because of possible crocodiles. But Livingston showed no fear and entered the water, clothes and all, assuring us that there was nothing to fear from American crocs. Sharks were more dangerous, he said. After he had braved the stream for about thirty feet and was not yanked under, George and I followed. With gear over our heads, we partly walked and partly swam to the other side, then rested dripping. Suddenly, a man in a dugout appeared out of the mangrove inlet. He was a young Seminole and Livingston apparently knew him.

His name was Tonto, he said, and he was after turtle eggs on the beach. After exchanging more friendly talk and sharing a cigarette with us, he nodded toward the cape and said "Are you going to Cape Sable? Big fish there scare tarpon. Even scared me."

It all sounded a trifle puzzling because Tonto spoke a broken English and we let it go at that. "Come on then," George said, "let's get going. You coming with us, Tonto?

The Indian nodded and ran down to the dugout, tying it to a big mangrove root.

When we finally reached Cape Sable my eyes bulged. The beach was an unbelievable scene. On it was loaded everything from coconuts and sea shells to giant skeletons of huge creatures. Livingston said the big bones belonged to whales that came ashore and became stranded. Here and there were huge head bones engulfed almost completely in sand, only the jawbones were showing. The beach was alive with shorebirds—black bellied plovers, knots, turnstones, yellowlegs.

Tonto had just turned over a large empty turtle shell when, suddenly, he pointed and yelled, "Fish!" Out in the green Gulf, my eyes caught the image of a mighty tarpon hurling itself into the air. It sparkled a second in the sunlight, twisted into an arch, then plunged into the sea. The sight triggered me into action.

I raced to my tackle box and in a few trembling minutes had surf rod and gear ready. I waded waist deep into the surf, took a firm

stance and heaved a four ounce, artificial lure into the sea and re-
trieved it quickly. Nothing happened. I made another cast, and another.
Ten times over I threw the gig into the sea and as many times nothing
happened. Tonto and Livingston watched me from the beach as they
smoked away. George took off up the beach exploring. At this moment there was a glimpse of two large fins cutting the surf about a
hundred feet to my left.

It was a giant sawfish—easily a dozen feet long and thick as a man
and armed with a four-foot flat saw-like snout. I let out slack line and
moved back quickly, noticing as I did a small school of baby sawfish
swimming feverishly in the shallows. Could the mother sawfish be
eyeing its young? Could I be an intruder? I bolted out of the surf,
happy only when my feet touched dry sand.

"What's the matter, son," questioned Livingston, "that sawfish
bothering you?"

"Well . . . well," I replied hesitantly, "let's just say that I don't
like the looks of things out there at this moment."

Tonto chuckled. Such things were common sights for him around
Cape Sable. Looking around, he found a large clam shell and heaved
it toward the monster. In his very best English, he uttered, "Hmm,
sawfish no scare me—sawfish scare tarpon."

The great fish glided past us, a huge glistening creature, part of
its tail and dorsal fins protruding from the shallow green sea. We
watched it for a long time until it finally vanished from sight well up
the beach. No sooner had this taken place when the water out in front
turned alive with wallowing porpoises. They were big, fat fellows and
barreled out of the water like bouncing tubs, puffing, and now and then
spraying the air with steam. We watched them cavort for several
minutes, after which they withdrew out into deeper water and passed
out of sight.

Unwilling to accept defeat I grabbed my rod and waded into the
surf. Once more I made a good heave and watched the lure drop just
beyond a point where the green water seemed to meet the blue. Suddenly something vicious struck. So powerful was the smash that for a

moment it drove me off balance and I nearly went down in the water to my knees. But I managed to recover and swiftly jerked the rod backwards. It took hold and immediately the rod arched and the reel screamed. The line went out against the drag, humming, and the spool lost volume quickly. I checked the rod and foolishly applied pressure to the reel, burning my thumb and unconsciously yelling, "Wow!"

Livingston heard me and called back, "Hold him son!" But there was no holding. Some great fish had felt the sting of the hook and was carrying it out to sea.

Again I tried to check him. This time, however, with the spool almost empty, the thing on the end turned into a wide circle. I pumped in the line, straining every inch to the tautness of a violin string. Then the line started through the water again piercing the surface with accelerating speed. Then came a spectacle: in a surging leap that carried him easily eight feet into the blue sky, the fish, a tarpon, made his first electrifying appearance. He came down in a quivering motion, landing on his tail with a thunderous splash, shaking his clapboard gills violently. No sooner had he landed when he shot back into the air again, still higher this time. I backed up, weaving, applying steady pressure on the rod. With all my strength I held him. But there was little chance to recover line, strong as it was, only to hold on.

Four times over this gladiator of Cape Sable struggled into the sun, his silver sides glistening like broken glass, and each time he hurtled buckets of spray into the sea around him. And just as many times he crashed dangerously back into the Gulf, smacking once with such force that I surely thought the hook would fly. But it held. Again he started another run, stronger than ever and turned into a wide semicircle, tugging and squirming. Once more his power surged and I sensed he was ready for another leap, and he came, his supple body twisting into a magnificent crescent, his form bent with insane savageness. I measured him quickly with sunburnt eyes—from snout to tail he was easily as long as a man. As he plunged down again in an enormous shower or spray, a delicate rainbow stood out for a brief moment, changed colors quickly, paled and disappeared.

When the tarpon broke through the foam he came at me too fast and I suddenly found myself with too much line. Panic gripped me. Livingston's voice rang out again: "Keep it tight, boy! *Keep it tight!*" George and Tonto hollered instructions, too.

Recovering quickly, I tightened the line once more and was relieved to know I still had him. Again I started to battle him, grinding away at the reel, gaining slowly and keeping the pressure on him. Then he sounded and I watched my hard-earned line give yardage once again. But he didn't stay down for long. For a while he bull-dogged near the bottom, then started upward in another rush. The sea cracked wide open once more as he propelled himself like a rocket into the wind, savage mouth gaping wide, fins spread like sails and body and tail thrashing in convulsive twists. At the height of the leap the silvery titan spun himself into a complete circle and dropped back into the waves, blasting a great white hole where he fell. The impact of the fall was so violent that I knew the hook would give this time. But by some miracle it held.

Finally, when I least expected it, I sensed the big fish give a little. The fight was turning. He was weakening. Frantically, as if some new power had been poured into my veins I started pumping again and the urge to conquer this great battler of the sea asserted itself.

Slowly the tarpon gave ground. But he wouldn't be hurried— not this bulldog of Cape Sable. He would still have to have his way. Obliquely he glided for ten yards, then a weak flip of his tail spun him into a roll and he headed in the opposite direction, pulling once more like a steer, lashing the water in barrel-round swells. I could see him plainly now . . . the huge head, large scales glistening in the sun, dark round eyes throwing me an accusing look. He still held a good 50 feet of my line but I was slowly and surely gaining on him. Foot by foot, inch by inch, he appeared to be *my* fish.

At this victorious moment I made a startling discovery. Fifty yards to my left the fins of the monster sawfish reappeared. A chill sweat broke out on my face and my heart pounded audibly. In a fit of desperation I lunged back on the rod. The tarpon rolled, a flourish of life still in him, but the sawfish was well aware of the dying struggle. Tonto screamed, *"Sawfish!"* Livingston's normally cool voice rose sharply. *"Great Lucifer, boy, careful!"* George yelled *"Watch it!"* I edged backwards, holding tight, one eye on the sawfish, the other on the tarpon. Then it happened.

Seeing the struggle coming to an end, the great sawfish rocketed a furious charge at the tarpon. On he came with frightening speed, his wicked saw skimming the water, tail fin splitting the surface like a bull tongue plow. So close to the beach was my fish now—only 30 feet—that instinctively I fell back, dragging the beaten fish with me. At this instant my foot gave way under a conch shell and I went down into the sea, thrashing, arms spread wide, but I recovered balance and was up in an instant. The sudden slack, however, sent my tarpon into another life-saving leap, and the hook flew. The sawfish was at the scene in a flash but was too late. So maddening was his swiftness to kill that it carried him just over the tarpon. He turned quickly in a wide arc and came back to the place of the encounter, but the tarpon was gone—free once more in the green dazzling sea from whence he came.

Waist-deep in water, bewildered, and utterly exhausted, I watched the sawfish cruise away and vanish.

I gathered myself together and began the painful walk to the beach. George was deadpanned, said nothing. Livingston and Tonto were standing together at the water's edge, sympathetic. "That's all right, my boy," the old man said, "you had him licked."

Tonto smiled weakly and shook his head. "Sawfish scared the tarpon. That's all."

Then for the first time, it dawned on me just what the Indian from the Everglades had really meant and his native wisdom helped immeasurably to take the sting out of my fallen vanity.

THE COLORFUL CHANGING FOREST

IT WAS AN UNUSUALLY WARM AUTUMN DAY WITH EVERY EVIDENCE THAT the trees of the hardwood glen had held their colorful leaves for a long time. The white birches were still bathed in soft yellows, the hickories in gold, the maples and linden in delicate coral and crimson. Here and there a sweetgum was enveloped in vestments of purple-red. But as the afternoon waned it grew cloudy and breezes came and soon the whole forest was buffeted on all sides by unruly winds. Most maple leaves showed their golden undersurfaces and a few began dropping in erratic fluttering flight to the earth.

That evening the rains came. They were strong and pelted the hardwood glen and soon the whole area became enshrouded in wet blackness. During the night the rain churned itself into a wild northeaster and much water fell. The wind and the rain combined their strength and lashed away at the hardwood trees. By dawn, however, the worst of the storm was over. In the western sky there came the subtle hint of clearing day. By dawn the glen was full of light and across one ridge the first rays of sunlight glowed. For the first time now a changed landscape appeared. In one wild night the trees of the glen had lost their leaves and stood out bare—and alone. In less than twenty short hours the beautiful forest had dropped its raiment of colorful foliage and took on the somber nakedness of winter. Once again a lovely woodland community, a whole wondrous province of trees, had yielded to the inevitable process of natural seasonal change.

If there is any one central characteristic which identifies the deciduous forest—that great biome of nature where hardwood trees annually lose their leaves—it is change. More than any other phenomenon, it is this change which marks this special world with unusual charm and marvelous beauty—a place of much mood and melancholy and diversity and great complexity.

Although everything about this world seems a bit strangely mixed up, with man the primary alchemist, the results nevertheless are richness and profusion. More books and poems and musical lines have had their roots in this changing forest than in any other natural region, and for good reason.

The deciduous forest as we know it in the United States is a temperate eastern forest. It occupies predominantly one third of the United States and part of southeastern Canada. Blessed with an average yearly rainfall of about 40 inches with an excess of precipitation over evaporation and delightful seasonal changes from warm summers to cool or cold winters, it is a region with a yearly variation in length of days and nights as distinct as any natural ecosystem on earth.

The beauty of the eastern forest is not fully appreciated even though it seems that nearly everyone in the east wants to live in it, or at least have a part of it. Unthinking man is the culprit. In all states, where the deciduous forest flourishes man is deliberately waging warfare against it. Many forest managers are committing wholesale tree murder with the use of chemical poisons which snuff out young trees in the matter of a few hours. The latest death-dealing weapon is a hatchet-chemical injector which when used efficiently by one operator will allow the wholesale killing of a thousand trees a day. The operator whacks into a tree, releases a shot of cacodylic acid, repeats the act two more times and a six inch aspen or maple tree is poisoned to death. This deliberate genocide of trees and whole hardwood forests is being done on a wide scale and in the name of timber stand improve-

ment, and with the encouragement of our federal and state governments. This is being done without sufficient facts as to what these
chemical poisons are doing to other trees, other plants, soil, wildlife,
fishlife and man himself. While it is true that, so far, few immediate
short-term ill effects have been noted, the concern of ecologists is over
what the long term dangerous effects might be. Surely there is need
for fuller evaluation of our chemical destroying methods or man as a
species may so contaminate his environment that his own very survival
may be placed in jeopardy.

In preglacial times our eastern forest was somewhat similar to that
of western Europe and central China. But with the advent of the ice ages
and, more recently, man with his axe, fire, plow, bulldozer, and now
chemical poison hatchets and injectors, many noticeable, even dramatic, changes have come about. Today this forest region has been so
altered by man that it is difficult to perceive and understand what
the original forest was like, much less what has happened and is still
happening to it. Fortunately, however, the more perceptive foresters
and ecologists who study this diverse and extremely complicated biome,
are discovering from their observations some reliable facts on what has
taken place.

The average person may not be deeply interested in the ecology
of the deciduous forest yet, if he lives in it or makes visits to it, he is
affected and so moved by the natural events that take place.

The beech-birch-maple forest, for example, is a type that forms
one of the climaxes in the northern deciduous forest. Once such forest
communities covered most of the east. But today clearing for various
reasons has been so extensive that many sections no longer can be
considered a distinct part of this original natural world.

A close look at our changing forest, as with most other forests,
will show that woods possess a certain pattern of layering or stratifica-
tion. Each layer, from the sub-floor and ground layer to the immediate
understory, through the central story and up across the top canopy,
is marked on separate zones of light, temperature, and moisture. Correspondingly, too, each zone possesses its special form of animal life.

Thus, a woodland is a series of plant and animal communities and, in a larger sense, a forest is a series of woodland communities. Some parts of the forest are special habitats, or niches, and certain plant and animal forms occupy them. These restricted or microhabitats are important to the life of certain animal species, like the ovenbird, for without them they could not exist.

My own life has been one of largely living in the eastern deciduous forest and, while I've made periodic sojourns to other fascinating worlds of nature, somehow I continue to spend much of my time in it. What is the attraction? What holds me in this forest? Well, I'm not sure I really know. But all things considered, I do know that nature puts on her best shows here, be it in the form of fascinating animal performances, wildflower shows, or the great spectacles that come with the changing of the seasons. And that's enough for me.

But the shows I speak of are not special performances for man. One must develop the desire to see and know them and one must be willing to play the role of participant as well as observer. In short, it means going out to see nature. The beauty and majesty of falling meteorites, for example, does the would-be on-looker little good if he is in the house watching a video box. The springtime marsh marigold does not go on blooming forever and goes unnoticed unless someone makes an effort to go to the wooded swamp to see it. So to know the deciduous forest, one must try to see it often—or as often as time permits.

At the University of Michigan I once had a genial professor of wildlife management, a perceptive man who instructed his class in a very informal manner in his own office. His main point was to stimulate within the student an interest in nature so as to make him want to go out-of-doors to observe, for he believed strongly in what Goethe once said: "Let nature do her teaching."

As a result of the professor's homespun philosophy, I found myself more than once in coolish spring woods learning to be observant. I could have stayed in my room, of course, and enjoyed a longer night's sleep. But the wildlife was in the woods and that was the place to see it.

As Professor Howard Wight used to say, "It's out there! You must make the effort to see it."

One spring evening I spread out my sleeping bag in a beech woods and went to bed. Because I had come for a purpose, I awoke from a fretful sleep often and just as many times raised my head repeatedly to listen. Nothing stirred. There was only the soft whisper of the breeze in the oaks and maples and the purr of moving air in the hemlocks. Finally, after much restlessness, I rolled onto my side from where I knew I could get a better view of things and closed my eyes.

How long I had slept, I do not know, but the sound that awoke me was enough to startle a dead man. Like an old Model T trying to start on a cold morning, it came . . . and then I saw it. There in plain view, in the early dawn, on the big log, he was. His wings were spread and soon he commenced to flail the air like a huge wasp.

When the first great flutter of wings was over, the bird cocked his head back and forth, then slowly folded his ruffled feathers and walked a few steps on the drumming log. At this point he made a left face, braced his fantail against the log and began to swell. He was commencing to drum again and I stopped breathing.

Slowly his chest puffed out, swelled, eyes fiery and flashing like shiny black beads, and his wings stretched way out. Again the action came, at first a slow, slam, slam of the air with powerful wings. Then a faster and faster flutter until all was motion and roar.

Again and again the *boom . . . boom . . . boom, boom, boom, boom . . . brrr, rrr, rrr* broke the spring woods, and each time I felt enormous chills come over my spine. Then a blue jay sounded its alarm and a moment later several crows called from still deeper woods. My performer, a ruffed grouse, slipped off the log and vanished and was never seen again. But I saw and heard him. I made the effort.

If any sound is representative of eastern woodlands it is, I believe, the drumming of the male ruffed grouse. While the intriguing sound is associated primarily with the mating ritual of the grouse, I have heard it in other seasons: once in the Maine woods in October when there were three inches of snow on the ground and another time in the Alleghenies in late summer after the young had hatched and were partially grown.

The ruffed grouse is a typical bird of eastern woodlands and its drumming heralds a change in the seasons. The sound proclaims to all who would listen that a big natural show is beginning. But nature's shows just don't come into your living room. So to see and hear a ruffed grouse perform on a drumming log is a rare treat and to become an audience to one or several such rare experiences requires a measure of "putting out," as Professor Wight used to say. I was a witness to a drumming grouse only this one time and it was well worth all the discomforts and anxieties produced by a cold night and a poor sleeping bag.

When the grouse begins to drum, other marked changes begin to take place in the deciduous forest.

Spring steals into the forest in different ways. In the woods of lower New England, for example, the russet leaves of the skunk cabbage are among the first plants to show life. The willows begin to display their yellow-green tinge and the song of the redwing is heard in the wet places. As spring days advance, more and more plants awaken. Animals, too, come alive.

One early May in southern Michigan, near Dryden, I had an occasion to visit a particular woodland swamp. The timing was perfect for the showy marsh marigold. In New England these wildflowers are called *cowslips*. So strikingly butter-gold were the flowers and so extensively spread through the watery woods that an aura of gold reflected in every direction. As far as you could see, the swamp was filled with marsh marigold. I was with friends, Mr. and Mrs. Ripley Schemm and Ed Brigham, and so moving was the spectacle that each of us simply stood there transfixed for some time drinking in the wonder of the bursting woods.

An hour later in an area of slightly higher ground along a wooded lane, we discovered patches of yellow violets and acres of fresh yellowish green grass. These plants were literally glowing in the woods. And in the more delicately shadowed woodlands the forest floor was alive with wild adder's-tongue. Some of the plants were already in flower. Another name for these delicate flowers is trout lily. They are a sensitive, quickly-vanishing species that permit one to see them only for short periods. Further in the thicker woods were giant white trilliums, a few here, a clump there, then more and still more. Finally at one point thousands adorned the damp woods. They glistened white everywhere, and around the trilliums, including the purple species, sprouted mayapples, small green parasols that soon would take over and turn these deciduous woods into a sea of luxuriant green.

Three weeks later I returned to these same woods. The trout lilies were gone. So were most of the flowers of the marsh marigold. Now wild phlox was taking over and blue violets and wild geraniums. In the same woods where the trilliums bloomed earlier, the mayapples were now a foot to eighteen inches high and some were just beginning to show their flowering buds. Although white trilliums still made the woods a place of great beauty, their days were ebbing. A young graduate student, Doug Scott, was with me that day and we began taking pictures, trying hard to capture the great lushness of spring. As we parted away masses of loose mayapple leaves, we made quite a discovery. Out from the moist earth sprouted morels—first one and two, then a few more, then a larger clump. They were large and succulent and tanned like fresh sponges. This was the finest and largest stand of morels I had ever seen and the excitement it brought to us was amazing. I know a photographer could tremble before a rare photographic shot of a deer or a fox, but morels—well, that was different. Since morels are fungi, and exceedingly tasty when cooked, picking the tempting bodies does little damage to the supply, so we gathered several hatfuls. Then we just stood there admiring our harvest. One particular morel was a magnificent specimen and measured five inches in height. It was fat and as fresh as any I had ever seen. Nature had quietly revealed her beauty and providence and we were there just in time to capture it.

Spring arrives at different times in different parts of the eastern forest. Edwin Way Teale in his delightful book, *North with the*

Spring, says that nobody knows exactly where spring begins. In the southern United States it starts before the March 21 vernal equinox and takes on the form of a slow awakening somewhere in the distant Everglades. Advancing northward about 15 miles a day and slowly gaining momentum, it gradually becomes more pronounced, picks up speed and soon rushes forward as a full awakening. Finally, somewhere in the heart of the temperate zone, at some certain point in time, it bursts forth in a blaze of full glory. The magnificent phenomenon—spring —is indeed a miracle and only the cessation of the miracle, as Longfellow once put it, would be equally miraculous.

Spring is the line between winter and summer and is many things to many people: the hidden yearning of the angler to be on a trout stream; the farmer seeding his new crop; the homeowner setting out plants around the house; the romping of children and their joyous voices in the yard or in the street; the stroll of young lovers in the park. The new season is the unfolding of leaves and the bursting of blossoms and the smell of freshly plowed earth, the song of the wood thrush once again in the glen, the mimical chirpings of the mockingbird in the tulip tree. It is the miracle of birth on a great stage.

Botanically, of course, the great miracle is photosynthesis, that unique power which green plants have of building up from very simple elements the more complex substances of plant body. The green plant secures water from the soil and the carbon dioxide from the air, and with the aid of the sun's energy, produces sugar. How the green plant is able to create and manufacture food for itself and for storage, which in turn can be used by animals and man, no one has been able to fully explain, for to know the mystery of creation in the leaf is to know the mystery of life itself.

We do know this, however: only green plants can make their own food; animals cannot. Plants can live without animals but animals cannot live without plants. This is the most important distinction between typical plants and typical animals. Yet this does not necessarily distinguish *all plants* from *all animals*. There are several large groups of plants, like bacteria and the fungi, which are unable to make foods

and depend upon other plants or animals for food. Molds and mushrooms are good examples.

The synthesis of living material to form food is a very complicated chemical process yet, in the spring, when the earth warms up and the sun's energy rays are more direct, growth takes place with great rapidity, though in a very organized manner. Growth is cell division followed by cell enlargement. Cells divide and redivide, some mature as support cells, some secrete protective layers of wax, others divide and become storage places for food. It is in this food storage ability that we find plants so important to man and animals. It seems almost ironical when we consider that man, who has learned to split the atom, fly to the moon, and do other great things, has yet to find a way to make food. He can extract food, he can change it around, he can help nature grow it, but he himself cannot synthesize it. Man who has learned to fly faster and farther than any bird, who has done wonders in technology and medicine and chemistry, is still powerless to create a living cell, is still dependent on the green chloroplast of the plant for his food.

The dependence of animals upon plants and the interdependence and interrelationships of plants to animals is one of the basic concepts of ecology. While more needs to be known of the complex role that plants play on earth and how they add to and sustain the gaseous supply of life-giving oxygen on earth, enough is known now to believe that outside of the green seas, trees, as dominant plants, are the principal supplier of photosynthetic oxygen in our green world. When we understand better the role of plants and our own relationship to plants and animals, then life and its meaning certainly comes clearer into focus. Only now, too, are we beginning to discover how important trees and other living plants are to urban environments—in pollution control and reduction of noise, in lowering temperature, and providing psychic release to people.

To many if not most people the loveliest of nature's plant kingdoms is the ever-changing eastern woodland. This old and incredible forest region where the broadleaved trees put out their fresh green leaves in the spring and then lose them again each autumn—this world of the ruffed grouse, gray squirrel, chipmunk, red fox, red maple, and redbud—is the acme of the living green world, the highest, most complex of our plant provinces on the continent, if not in the world.

And just as the sound of the grouse is typical of our eastern woods, so too are certain trees, the oaks, birches, hickories, beech, yellow poplar, sycamore, ironwood, the gums, ashes, and the maples typical deciduous trees. All lose their leaves, all make the annual cycle of growth, change, dormancy, and rebirth.

There are, of course, the evergreen trees, the hemlock, red and white cedar, and the pines—white, red, pitch, and in the South the five hard pines (loblolly, shortleaf, longleaf, slash, and Virginia). There are also the two kinds of annual needle-shedding softwoods, the tamarack and the baldcypress. But most evergreens in the eastern forest are so-called temporary species. Sweep any area clean of trees in the typical deciduous forest and what does nature come back with—hardwoods. The pines that come back are only temporary and when the competition stiffens, give way to the broadleaved trees. Trees then are plants of great wonder.

But what really is this extraordinary plant we call *tree* and, among the more than 200 species present, is there one that most universally represents the changing forest?

A tree, according to botanists and foresters, is a single-stemmed woody plant which attains normally a height of at least twenty feet. A shrub or bush on the other hand is a plant with many stems and, while woody, does not usually grow higher than twenty feet. Thus a maple is a typical tree and a many-stemmed speckled alder is a shrub.

Strange as it may seem living trees are mostly dead tissue. Only a a small percentage of a tree is alive—the buds, leaves, cambium and root tips. The cambium is a single-celled sheath of living substance just inside the bark and branches. This amazing vital ring constantly renews itself adding cells to the inner bark and the sapwood. As the older layers of the sapwood cease to function they become dead cellulose and another "annual growth ring" is added to the tree trunk. Once each autumn the leaves fall off from the so-called "hardwood" trees while in the conifers or evergreens, the process of leaf shedding is "a little at a time." Year in and year out the tree thickens, branches get bigger, the crown heightens and the roots grow longer. Thus, each growing season all parts of the tree are renewed and strengthened.

All trees are different. Even those of the same species can be exceedingly varied. When I was a forestry student and worked during three summers on Dutch elm disease control, I probably climbed a thousand suspicious-looking elm trees and never found two alike. Yet there is enough similarity in trees to make their identification relatively easy. The secret lies in learning the important distinguishing characteristics. First must come the viewpoint, usually the far-off view, then the closer look and, finally, the detailed scrutiny.

Perhaps no tree represents the changing eastern woods like the maple. Although several lesser species occur in the biome, like box-elder and mountain and striped maple, it is the sugar maple and the red or soft maple that dominate the native forests of the east. The sugar or hard maple is predominantly a tree of the northeast and of the uplands while the soft maple occurs all through the east, especially in the lowlands, and reaches as far south as the Everglades. It is the maples which brighten up the woods in the spring with their red buds and give us such vivid colors in the leaves in the autumn.

When trees combine into plant communities to make up woods or forests they form into important photosynthetic systems taking vast amounts of carbon dioxide gas and releasing oxygen. Forests, then, because of their important gaseous exchange are important for the survival of animals. Samuel T. Dana, perhaps America's most noted present-day forester and dean-emeritus of the University of Michigan School of Natural Resources, has said that while perhaps we can live without woods we cannot survive without forests. And today urban ecologists are also saying that, no city can survive without trees.

During the summer months the deciduous forest consolidates the gains which it has made during the spring. The growth of fast-developing sapwood of trees slows down to become denser cellulose and lignin, leaves lose their shine, and woodland wildflowers take on stronger colors. Over the surface of the forest floor and below it there is feverish activity. It is a kind of nature's workshop where thousands of creatures, uncommissioned by humans, build, dig, spin, repair, devour, and keep everything in order. Bacteria are busy breaking down animal and vegetable material with some fungi sending out colorful fruiting bodies in the form of mushrooms, to the delight of wood turtles, slugs, and mushroom gatherers, and students of fungi. Nothing is useless, nothing unimportant, nothing independent.

Consider the lowly earthworm in his summer subterranean burrow. Some 50,000 of them wiggle through any acre of soil. In twenty years they carry from the sub-soil to the surface a layer of rich soil three inches deep. Not only does this lowly creature move soil but it improves it through its own digestion, not to mention the invaluable aeration it provides the soil. Other creatures help, too—beetles and ants, salamanders, frogs, snakes, shrews, and mice. All are making a contribution in the forest for, like the birds of the various strata and the larger mammals, they are part of the whole dynamic forest community. But then one day the workshop slows down and another season comes. Autumn is on the way.

In my book, our eastern autumns come slowly, hesitatingly, as if there were "maybe" in the dawn's coolness, "perhaps" in the night's chill. The red maple's leaves become edged with red, while a nearby oak remains fresh and youthfully green. Morning glories trail from fences, while an autumnal painter touches the empty fields where, in spots, goldenrods wave in the thin sunlight.

If one can be out in the country in late September and take time to drive the by-roads where forests and fields intermingle, he may be well rewarded for his effort. Although spring is normally the season for wildflowers, the real spectacles in floral artistry come in the autumn and, in particular, in fields which were once forests and which are again left for a season or two and show signs of forest regeneration.

One of the most amazing floral sights I have ever seen took place recently in Virginia. So overpowering was the scene that I had to stop to admire it and photograph it. As I did so, the traffic on Route 7 continued to roar by, with most drivers and passengers perhaps wondering what I was up to. Spectacular fall beauty in the commonplace yet few people had the trained eye to see it. Had someone taken time to call Washington residents' attention to this sight, I daresay northeastern Virginia would have had a hundred thousand extra visitors on that weekend. It was the third week of September, a place not too distant from the Dulles International Airport. Here, vast expanses of unmowed fields were being taken over by the tick seed sunflower to give a massive golden glow to acre upon acre of fields and uncropped pastureland— forming the most extensive, most solid carpet of flaming wildflowers I have seen anywhere. So far-reaching and illuminating was the scene that a heavy glow of gold was cast far across the landscape.

But it is in October—the showiest month of all autumn months— when the artistry of mother nature reveals her most beautiful paintings and brings her picture book to a dramatic climax. While scientists know much about plant pigments, in many cases what pigments are used, what techniques are employed and followed to make it what it is, only the Great Painter himself can disclose. Botanists advance a partial answer but not the complete one, and with this explanation we must be satisfied. The more mysterious and hidden secrets of plant physiology remain locked, perhaps forever, in the book of the unknown.

They say that in October one must think in terms of chlorophyll, the stuff that is made of several pigments. Along with the two green chlorophyll pigments in the leaves there are also yellow pigments—the carotene and the xanthophylls. These are masked by the chlorophyll. When nights are cold but not necessarily frosty, and the days are mild and sunny, chlorophyll, like drapes in your living room that have had too much sun, fades and the yellow pigments become prominent. The condition in the leaf inhibits the daily transfer of the small amount of sugar formed; hence, there is some accumulation in the leaf. Through chemical changes in the leaf, associated with the sugars, red or bluish anthocyanin pigments appear. The varying combination of these pigments in leaves of different kinds of plants give us the glorious pageant of October. The sombre brown of the leaves of some plants is due to tannin within the leaf.

So it is the fading of chlorophyll and the accumulation of sugars and the various pigments (carotene, xanthophylls, anthocyanin) which impart the bright colors to fall foliage. More than this is little known. But why worry? Is it not sufficient that autumn colors are beautiful, that man and all that walks or sings or chirps is affected? Take the cricket for instance. His rhythmic chirpings in the eaves are now slowed to an occasional *"errp."* His day is done. The young of the bob-white in the lespedeza patch are grown. The parents and their off-spring now band together in a single covey, all twittering joys of delight over bountiful seeds of beggarweed. The barking gray squirrel in the yellow hickory tree or the red oak, rushes around hiding his winter food supply in some wooden storage box. The raccoon and wood-chuck and black bear simply eat and eat to put on a cold weather supply of hog fat, important excess calories that will be exhausted long before the warming rays of the March sun come again. The elusive red fox feels the cool night air and flexes his spirited legs, and woe to the walker hounds who would give him chase.

As the season advances the ducks and geese awaken to an inner urge and take off with their full-grown young for parts further south where the food is more lasting. Up they go, up and over the many-colored fields and woods, up and over the great hardwood forests, onward to the warmer climes. If you are out there and have good eyes, you can mark their direction. They don't tarry long. They'll be over some dark cornfield in a minute and, like the autumnal winds, their streaming silhouettes will soon remain but a shadow in your memory.

But one coolish morning you awaken and find that the autumn that was has surrendered to the cold, and the conflict ends. The sun rises red from behind purple cloudbanks and the temperature plummets. This is the beginning period of slumber for oak and gum, beech and birch. The chipmunk and the woodchuck prepare for a deeper sleep. The fox—both the red and the gray—must now search more strenuously for their food. Only the evergreens, eternally fresh looking, touch the woodland with life. On the creekbank soft cattails ride on stilt-like stems and along the roadside the cornstalks are brown and broken.

The moon now rises big and orange and floats high and loose as if filled with hydrogen. The landscape turns ash gray with splashes of luminous ivory and the dry light wine of a fading day kindles a rare intoxication. Autumn is definitely gone. Winter is here.

When the final deep cold descends upon the deciduous forest everything is soon wrapped into a chilling white cloak, and all the trees become a bit frosty. Occasionally the season, like an artful baker, fancifully decorates a cake, and spreads its frosting of ice and snow with subtle artistry, endowing familiar scenes with breath-taking beauty. A wet snowfall loads the trees and shrubs with white blankets, turns them into feathery plumes; a sleet storm coats the woods with a film of glass that sparkles like crystal in the sunlight; a howling blizzard makes the trees creak and crack.

The deciduous forest in the winter is dominated by distinct trees. In warm weather, trees are a great mantle of green and it is difficult to tell one from the other. Pines merge with oaks, hemlock and redcedar blend with sugar maple and black birch. Even the cypress of our more southern forests diffuses with an ocean of green shade. They are forests in which individual trees are far too seldom noted. But now all is changed. Now all is reversed. Now individual trees make up the deciduous forest. The steel-gray trunk and branches of the beech are unmistakable. The elms rise upward spreading out like beautiful flower vases. The white birches on the hillside are as supple as ballerinas. The great oaks now show a ruggedness and power as never before. In the lowlands the gray crowns of the sweet gum are separate and distinct.

Winter gives stark beauty and individuality to trees. The hickory stands boldly alone, its scaly trunk now clearly discernible in the open woods. Along stone wall fences the sugar maple stands steadfast, tree after tree, each solid, each one silent. Nearby, in the lowlands, individual stately tulip poplars rise majestically into the upper sea of forest branches. Here and there the fluted-trunks of sassafras stand out, clear and cold; so too the dogwood, the heavy limbed catalpa, the full-stemmed tree-of-heaven. They are trees now, separate and solemn, and all waiting—waiting for the season to turn as it inevitably must turn, for this is the changing deciduous forest and change as always is its password.

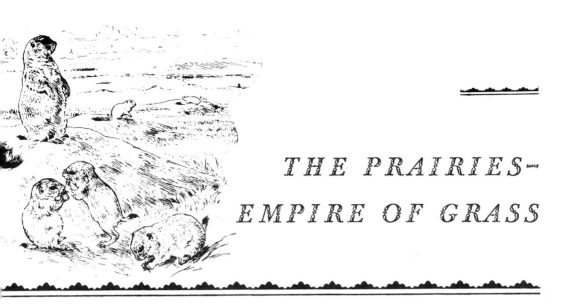

THE PRAIRIES—
EMPIRE OF GRASS

FOR SEVERAL MINUTES THE BIG-EYED CREATURE STOOD HIS GROUND, SILENT and immutable, an elegant silhouette against the prairie sky. Not a muscle stirred in him and not a hair ruffled his tawny form. Suddenly, a nerve registered in his curious brain, and he dropped his head for a better look. Then, cautiously, he slowly eased two steps forward.

For a long time the object of his study, a man, stared back at him, much as an infantryman eyes his adversary to make a false move. Only this man had no gun. He had come to the short-grass plains not to kill wildlife but to photograph it. And luck was apparently with him. Were it not for the brow of the hill and a clump of buffalo grass, he would have been perfectly exposed and the pronghorn would have been off.

Again the stare; again the vigil. Now the antelope was holding his head high, eyes and ears fixed, nostrils testing the Wyoming wind. He was not in the best position for a photograph, so the photographer decided on a stunt—to hurl a rock toward him and register a touch of the dramatic on film. The trick worked. This time curiosity got the best of of the antelope and he advanced several more steps and then threw his head into a high alert position—a beautiful form against the western sky—and held. But only one click of the shutter was all he would oblige and he was off in a startled lope to join the rest of the herd, now all running, down the range. The group darted this way and that way for a hundred yards and stopped. Then, once more, each animal eyed the place from whence the disturbance came.

When I, the photographer, finally stood up and snapped an action shot, the pronghorns put a lot of grassland between us and disappeared into the shadows of the golden hills. They were a marvelous band of agile creatures and I felt spirited myself as I saw them move with grace and beauty across the plains.

If anything typifies the short-grass prairies of the West, it is the American pronghorn and, of course, the bison. The antelope is not a true antelope, however, but a pronghorn and a dweller of the open plains. Indigenous to the grasslands, he is an integral part of its community of life. And like the millions of bison that once roamed the Great Plains from northern Mexico and the Texas panhandle northward into Canada and eastward from the Rocky Mountains to the Dakotas, Nebraska, Kansas, Oklahoma and further eastward, the pronghorn filled the original plains country to the overflowing. Yet unlike the buffalo, which never came back after their original extirpation, the pronghorn returned strong. Conservation laws, good range management, and the fact that the antelope was more compatible to modern range use, all worked in its favor. Today, the antelope once again can be seen on the plains while the buffalo has been reduced to small remnants in parks and refuges.

America's original prairies formed the finest biomes of grass and herbaceous vegetation in the entire world. Only in the Pampas of Argentina and the Steppes of Russia was there anything faintly resembling it. Of the original 1,900,000,000 acres that constituted the land area of the United States, roughly two-thirds or 770,000,000 acres were grassland—vast western short-grass ranges, mid-grass prairies, tall-grass prairies, and the mixed transitional zone of open meadows and eastern woodlands.

It seems a little ironical today that man, who began his civilization in the grasslands of the Middle East, should destroy them and, as a result, hasten the demise of his own civilization. With goats and sheep,

fire and plow, man attacked his grasslands and when they could bear no more, his own survival came to the test. While this has not yet occurred in America, it is nevertheless true that we have seriously exploited and destroyed much of our once great empire of grass.

In the days of the original West the grasslands and prairies carried an infinite variety of plants. Grass species numbered into the hundreds, thriving under varied but good conditions of soil, elevation, and climate. Under the wide blue sky of the mid-west, in the lowlands, grew the meadow grasses of the woodland prairies, big bluestem, little bluestem, Indian grass, and switchgrass. In the drier upland clearings, where the wild hooved animals grazed and the Indians made their settlements, the prairie grasses were shorter but nonetheless elegant and seemingly always waving in the wind.

Further westward, where the oak trees dropped out for lack of sufficient moisture, stretched the central grasslands, mile upon mile, a wide belt of yellow and gold and brown in some 200 million acres strong. Some of this country grew grass perennials that lasted many seasons and showed up heavy and thick like wheat. And further to the west lay the mixed prairie soil builders, such as the western wheatgrass and needle-and-thread, often called the mid-grasses, and the shortgrasses such as blue grama and buffalo-grass. And still farther westward, over the intermountain west, stretched the bunchgrasses such as the bluegrasses, fescues, and wheatgrasses. Each grass had its own special characteristics, its own limits of soil, its limits of moisture, its resistance to grazing. The mixed prairies, the largest of the grassland-prairies, rolled out far and wide, like a golden flame from coastal Texas to Alberta. Just east of this prairie was the tall-grass country, the most beautiful of all the prairie lands in America.

Plains Wildlife

So extensive was the American grassland before the white man's coming that its chief grazers, the buffalo, numbered into the millions. The basic food chain in those days was a simple one—780 million acres of prairie land with good soils that supported good grasses, that sup-

ported prodigious herds of buffalo, that supported perhaps 300 thousand plains Indians.

The great drama behind America's original grasslands is, of course, the saga of the buffalo—its once great numbers, its pillage, and its sudden, almost total obliteration from the American landscape.

The buffalo roamed wherever there was grass, including lush grass valleys of the eastern deciduous forest. New York's Lake Erie shore and central Pennsylvania once knew buffalo. Virginia's Shenandoah Valley and Big Lick (now Roanoke) supported many buffalo before 1750. I have seen old buffalo trails in Kentucky and walked some of them in Tennessee.

The native buffalo range was wide and extensive. It stretched from almost the Atlantic seaboard to Nevada and eastern Oregon, from Mexico to near the shores of Great Slave Lake, supporting a population of wild ungulates such as no other continent had ever seen. Yet in a mere 60 years man—white man—almost totally destroyed this great wildlife legacy. And on top of it all, a terrible mortal blow was delivered to the primitive plains Indian.

To know something of the numbers of buffalo on the mid-grass and short-grass plains west of the Mississippi River, one need only to become familiar with the exploits of such men as George Catlin, Howard Stansbury, and Colonel R. I. Dodge. What these men saw and reported is head-shakingly hard to believe. There was the instance of the *Sioux* group who in one foray killed 1,400 buffalo only for their tongues, for there was ample dry buffalo meat on hand. There were other episodes where great slaughters were made merely for the choice tenderloins along the backbone of the animals or the tripe of young cows.

In the heyday period the prairie-lands buffalo moved in enormous colonial hordes. W. A. Ferris in pushing westward across the Platte River reported the plains dark with buffalo and this for miles and miles. Not only was the grassland covered with black objects, he reported, but actually crowded with them. Even as late as 1871 Colonel Dodge reported driving for twenty-five miles through an immense aggregation of animals on his way from Old Fort Zara to Fort Larned on the Arkansas River. The herd was 25 miles long and 50 miles deep and numbered an estimated four million head. The total population of the herd at that time was put at twelve million.

Buffalo meat is tasty and, unlike modern beef, low in fat content. Like caribou meat which is meaty and tender, it is all protein and delectable. One can, as I have experienced several times, fairly well indulge on it. The early plains Indians as well as the cavalry-borne soldiers and the settlers who came to expel them often gorged themselves on buffalo meat. A ration for a hard-riding cavalryman was an incredible eight pounds of buffalo meat per day. A young tough Indian brave at an evening's great buffalo feast, interrupted only by periodic strenuous dancing but no indigestion, could consume as much as twenty pounds of buffalo meat.

The simple grass-protein-Indian relationship was bound to go and it did go before the westward push. What broke the plains were the gun, the railroad spike, the bull tongue plow and barbed wire.

The grasslands of America once supported perhaps sixty million buffalo. Yet by 1889, within the lifetime of many still living, they were almost totally decimated, leaving a tiny vestige of only 600 animals of the original herd. The most terrible destruction came from professional hunters who shot buffalo for hides and horns. The worst destruction occurred in only twenty years, between 1865 and 1884.

Though the great buffalo herds probably had to go one way or another, several questions remain: Did this wildlife have to go so dramatically and so completely? And if so, what lesson, if any, did man learn? When one sees the wholesale poisoning of prairie dogs on today's western plains or the death-dealing use of pesticides and herbicides on today's animal and plantlife, one must ask if man has learned anything about wildlife ecology in spite of the great sophistication he has achieved.

A hundred years to destroy a vast empire of grass and fifty years to decimate its wildlife! It seems unthinkable. Yet it happened. Today most of the tall-grass prairies are farmlands. Much of the original prairie peninsulas and oak savannahs are covered by sprawling cities and suburbs. Millions upon millions of acres of original sodlands have been plowed under, others covered by concrete and asphalt, still others tilted for drainage. Other millions of prairie acres have been irrigated for crops. Vast acreages of open range have been burned, overgrazed, or covered over by roads and highways. Since 1880 the original grasslands of the United States have shrunk by 300 million acres. In recent years more than 15 million acres of the Great Plains range have been plowed —turning under vast areas of original buffalo-grass, blue grama, wheat-grasses, and a host of other range grasses. According to some agronomists, many of the acres should never have been plowed. Range ecologists who have studied the problem of overgrazing and grassland management point out the folly of plowing under many acres of marginal, delicately-balanced, critical environments.

When the English colonists settled at Jamestown in 1607, the Southwest was already being grazed by sheep, horses, and cattle brought into the country by the Spaniards. Even Florida was being grazed prior to the settlement of St. Augustine in 1565. Thereupon the assault on our grasslands took a three-pronged attack—a northward expansion in the Southwest, a mighty movement northwestward from the South, and a relentless push into the West from the eastern seaboard. After 1830 western livestock production skyrocketed—the eastern meat growers had met the Texas herdsmen moving northward. By 1890, with Indian wars over, the building of the western railroads and the Civil War things of the past, there were 26 million cattle and 20 million sheep in the 17 western states. The great, once seemingly inexhaustible grasslands of the West, had reached the ultimate in carrying capacity of the prairies.

But the total exploitation of the grasslands was yet to come. Around the turn of the century and up to World War I, a fierce competition developed for western range lands. More and more cattle came to the ranges. Sheep increased. Cattlemen and sheepmen met in open war on the range. Grass was free and the range land belonged to the man who got there first or who brought in the most cattle or who grazed the most sheep or who could graze the closest.

The Plow That Broke the Plains

On top of the fierce battles for the western range came the bull tongue plow, the twenty mule team, to "bust up" the sod and sow it to wheat and barley and oats. And then came the tractor, the mightiest "plains buster" of them all. Within a few decades 40 percent of the Great Plains country was virtually plowed under. By the 1920s and '30s dust storms and overgrazing were so devastating that something had to be done.

One spring day in 1935, in Washington, D. C., a big, burly man was testifying on a pending bill before a committee in Room 333, of the Senate Office Building in the Capitol. The measure would soon establish the Soil Conservation Service of the Department of Agriculture. The man was Hugh Hammond Bennett, who would soon rise to fame as the "Father of Soil Conservation."

On that day America's midsection was in trouble; so was the whole country! The somber telltale marks of the Big Depression were clearly evident everywhere.

In the Plains states the land groaned in drought-stricken agony. The winds howled and dust was all around—on the ground, in buildings, in the air. Airplanes above Oklahoma, Texas, Wyoming, Nebraska, and the Dakotas were struggling at 20,000 feet to find air free of dirt and sand. Ten-foot drifts of dust stopped highway and rail traffic. People lost their way in dark blizzards of floating soil a hundred yards from their home. The clatter of many hooves and the rumble of tractors were stilled. America's Dust Bowl was enjoying its finest hour.

Two of the duststorms had blown their way eastward 2,000 miles to pass over the nation's capital almost blotting out the sun, and to sweep out to the sea to settle on ship decks 300 miles offshore in the Atlantic.

On that appalling day, a grim shadow passed over the window of the hearing room. One Senator remarked, "It's getting dark." Another said, "Maybe it's dust."

It was dust. Hugh Bennett stood up and looked out the blurred window. "There, gentlemen," he said, "goes Oklahoma!"

Capitalizing on the formation of the U. S. Forest Service in 1905 and organized grazing experiments that began during the period 1910-1926, knowledge of range management grew and the conscience of America began to stir. But there was need of additional legislation. It came in the form of the McSweeney-McNary Forest Research Act in 1928, the formation of the Soil Erosion Service in 1933, and the passage of the Taylor Grazing and Soil Conservation District acts in 1937. And "Big Hugh" Bennett headed the new U. S. Soil Conservation Service when the name Soil Erosion Service was dropped. More than any man, Big Hugh aroused the nation to soil conservation and to effective programs of land and water conservation.

Today grazing is the largest single use of agricultural lands. In recent years approximately 900 million acres of pasture and range were classed as grazing lands. Of this total, more than 600 million acres are still in open grassland with nearly 250 million acres in wooded prairies. Five main groups of grassland ownership are presently noted in the United States. Approximately 70 percent continues in private ownership. The Bureau of Land Management administers another 14 percent, the U. S. Forest Service 8 percent, and 4 percent by the Bureau of Indian Affairs. State agencies administer another 4 percent.

According to my colleagues in the U.S.D.A., our great needs today in the grasslands and prairies of America are several: better utilization of existing grasslands, cessation of further deterioration of overgrazed and eroded lands, and the rebuilding of lands that have been plowed under, over-cultivated, or otherwise abused. What's more, they say, we need to save more grasslands for non-agricultural use, for wildlife, scenic beauty, recreation. We must also keep some lands *natural* for scientific and educational purposes. This one point seems especially important in view of our mounting population. Unless we have some large natural samples of our original prairies to see and study—and appreciate—how will future generations of Americans know what this country was like when it belonged to the buffalo and the Indian?

The Grassland Sea is a beautiful country—in a very distinct way. It is not simply endless acres of grass sweeping from horizon to horizon, though this may be found in places. It is much more. The Great Plains include the area often referred to as "the breadbasket of the nation," where vast areas are in private ownership. Much of this land is used for cultivated crops as well as for grazing. Grass country is usually treeless, a country of rolling plains with varying types of soils which dictate how the land may be used. Interspersed with the prairie heartland are fields of wheat and other grains, sorghums, alfalfa lowlands, and native meadows. And there are several areas in federal ownership as national grasslands.

The national grasslands are under the U. S. Forest Service and are generally the marginal lands within the national forests which have poorer soils that are not suitable for cultivation. Many of these suffer from past abuse, and are being restored to their original short-grass cover. Some of these areas are intermingled with privately-owned crop lands and livestock ranches.

Bountiful Biome to Preserve

In recent years much interest has centered around natural areas. The preservation of some original grassland areas has been the target of the Nature Conservancy and small prairie and plains "natural" areas have been preserved. On some of these lands the native grasses have been encouraged to return. In Ohio, where limited areas of open prairie were once a common sight, there is hardly a place left with original grass. Fortunately, a few people, like Paul Knoop of the Aullwood Audubon Center, have successfully brought back small parcels of once native grasses, like the twelve-foot big bluestem.

It is encouraging to learn, too, that a proposal is under-way to establish a Prairie National Park. The area being considered lies in the Flint Hills area in eastern Kansas. The prairie grasses the park hopes to preserve will include those generally found in the "bluestem country" with a limestone base. Not only will the various native grasses be preserved but also its biotic life—ground squirrels, prairie dogs, coyotes, foxes, the badger, perhaps the rare red wolf, antelope, buffalo and a host of grassland birds, like the prairie chicken; also native reptiles, fishes, and invertebrates.

Grass as a plant is an ageless part of the land. To the Indian grass was eternal, a changeless part of their country, and so it should be to us today. The primitive Indian gave way to civilization; cattle replaced buffalo; grasslands gave way to corn and wheat. But still as we relax amidst man-made luxuries, it is grass that somehow remains the permanent basic natural resource of our land.

When land is abused, it is grass that often remains—it endures in spite of man's folly, for it is the key to our whole system of agriculture. It is grass that is a factor in the delicate balance between failure and success. Remove or destroy the grass, as man did in Greece and Jordan and other impoverished lands, and the soil blows away. Then cattle and wildlife decline, and rainfall quickly runs off into silt-choked rivers. Use grass wisely, and the country yields an abundance of nature's ever-renewing wealth.

The story of early America is a testimony to the power of grass. Each chapter, colorful or tragic, is in large measure the saga of our heritage of grass.

In North America there were Indians and millions of buffalo; there were cattlemen and homesteaders who struggled in a land of uncertain crops. Across its central heartland passed prospectors, trappers, soldiers, railroad builders, and a host of other frontiersmen. They all helped to push back the wild America.

But mostly it was grass that subtly guided the fate of men. Sometimes grass was lush, and men prospered. Often it was overgrazed, plowed up, or burned by drought. Hard times followed. Still somehow, somewhere, some life remained in the land, and when this life showed up, it was grass that made the showing.

Perhaps the most eloquent testimonial to grass ever written came from the late U. S. Senator John J. Ingalls of Kansas. He once said:

Grass is immortal. Next in importance to the divine profusion of water, light and air, those three physical facts which render existence possible, may be reckoned the universal benefits of grass. Lying in the sunshine among the buttercups and dandelions of May, scarcely higher in intelligence than those minute tenants of that mimic wilderness, our earliest recollections are of grass. And when the fitful fever is ended, and the foolish wrangle of the market and the forum is closed, grass heals over the scar which our descent into the bottom of the earth has made, and the carpet of the infant becomes the blanket of the dead.

Grass is the forgiveness of nature . . . her constant benediction. Fields trampled with battle, saturated with blood, torn with the ruts of cannon, grow green again with grass, and carnage is forgotten. Streets abandoned by traffic become grass grown, like rural lanes, and are obliterated. Forests decay, harvests perish, flowers vanish, but grass is immortal.

Beleaguered by the sullen hosts of winter, it withdraws into the impregnable fortress of its subterranean vitality and emerges upon the solicitation of spring. Sown by winds, by wandering birds, propagated by the subtle horticulture of the elements which are its ministers and servants, it softens the rude outlines of the world. It invades the solitude of deserts, climbs the inaccessible slopes and pinnacles of mountains, and modifies the history, character, and destiny of nations. Unobtrusive and patient, it has immortal vigor and aggression.

It bears no blazonry of bloom to charm the senses with fragrance or splendor, but its homely hue is more enchanting than the lily or the rose. It yields no fruit in earth or air, yet should its harvest fail for a single year, famine would depopulate the world.

LAND OF THE DESERT SUN

WESTWARD BEYOND THE SHORT GRASS PLAINS, CRADLED BETWEEN THE Rockies and the Pacific coast ranges, lies the vast palmated form of the Great American Desert. Sparsely settled for the most part and largely a dry featured wilderness, it is a land beset by contrasts and striking natural loveliness.

The desert indeed can be and often is a beautiful place. Much depends on who the onlooker is and how trained his senses are to the natural world. One thing seems clear: the desert has no middle ground; one either loves it or hates it.

To love the desert one must stop long enough to see it and know it. This cannot be done simply by racing pell mell across a lot of space. Desert appreciation is a creative act and takes time.

In many ways the desert is an inhospitable environment, yet this again depends upon one's viewpoint. Surely it seems a little strange that man should choose the desert to begin his civilization. We know from history that when the wandering creature MAN ceased to roam as a nomad and commenced to build houses to live in villages, he chose to make his stake in the desert—in three areas of the desert. He picked the dry region of the Middle East between the Tigris and the Euphrates, the arid plains beyond the Indus, and the blistering sands along the river Nile. He could have chosen the verdant jungles of

Africa or the salubrious forests of the Americas, but he did not. Strange, too, it seems that Moses should seek the Promised Land in the desert and that Jesus should be born in the desert, in the dry land of Judea, to bring to the world the wisest of guidelines for living yet assembled.

Deserts are extensive. Nearly a third of the land surface of the earth is classified as arid, a region where the central characteristics are torrid heat and little rainfall—less than ten inches per year. All deserts, wherever they occur, the Sahara, Mongolia, Israel, Peru, Australia, or the Great American Desert, have several things in common. They are lands with dazzling sunlight, excessive heat and seemingly low, over-powering blue sky. They are quiet and somber lands where the sun is king and everything is baked to dull colors—pale yellows, parched greens and browns, purples, and mauve grays.

Deserts are exposed, naked lands, where the soil is thin and plants must fight for moisture much as animals, especially birds, struggle to stake out a territorial claim. They are lands marked by contrasts: oven-heat middays and cold, chilly nights; tranquil mornings and often violent windstorm afternoons; of long periods of unbearable dessication and occasional short torrential downpours and flash floods.

Desert lands, above all, are dry lands—the domain of the desert sun. There are riverbeds but in them no water runs. There are mudflats and sandbars and flood-plains but the streams that formed them are gone. Clouds gather in fleecy pillows overhead, shading huge sections of the landscape in purple but they release no rain.

The desert has other identifying features: big heavens, piercing heat, sparse vegetation, sandblasted rocks, and peculiar animals which have become especially adapted to live without drinking water.

But even in the desert there is some moisture. Short rains do come in seasons. Often these occur as cloudbursts, the runoff quickly filling dry rivulets and streambeds to the overflowing. Then just as suddenly as the rains had come, they stop. Floods race on down to the valleys, only to spread out, dry up, and disappear. Once more the desert is dry. Again the sun bakes with furnace heat. Once more there is the strong reminder that you are in a parched land.

Low humidity is common in the desert. Yet there are some exceptions, such as the "fog" desert zones of Africa and South America. These have moisture-carrying clouds and mists. Here very little or no rain falls. Along the edge of the Sahara the winter cloud cover is only ten percent; in the summer only four percent.

Many people believe that the tropical jungle is the hottest place on earth. However, facts do not bear this out. This distinction must go to the deserts of the world where very high temperatures have been recorded. The highest temperature ever recorded on earth in the shade was made in the Sahara—a record of 136° F. The United States record in Death Valley, in Southern California, stands at only two degrees less.

The sojourner in arid lands soon discovers that the desert loses its daytime heat astonishingly fast. This is because the dry air contains few water molecules. When the sun goes down, there is little moisture in the air to retain the heat, thus cold comes on quickly and surprisingly. Day and night temperatures may also vary greatly, ranging from scorching summers to freezing winters. The wise desert traveller, then, puts in a good stock of woolens as well as cottons.

The question is often asked how did the deserts come about? Are they old or new worlds? Geologists and weather experts who have studied the earth believe that the deserts are lands of comparatively recent origin, having developed over the past 15 million years. As our highest mountains uplifted and tilted, they created barriers for the winds sweeping across them. As winds with moisture-laden atmosphere move from west to east, they are deflected upward to get across the mountains. This results in the formation of cooler air, causing rains to fall on the windward slopes. As the winds pass over the mountain tops, they lose most of their moisture, thus little rain falls on the leeward slopes and even less on the valleys below. Some of the wettest regions of the world are found on the windward slopes of mountains, causing "rain forests" and, beyond these wettest, smaller worlds, lie some of our driest and largest deserts.

Some lands become deserts because they are far from the sea, the source of most moisture. Coastal winds tend to be warm because the ocean serves as a global thermostat, and as moist winds sweep inland they become cooler and bring rain. As these same winds move further and further inland, the rainfall gets correspondingly less and less until desert conditions prevail.

On the other hand there are deserts that lie very close to the sea, like the Negev in Israel. The reason given for this is the complex inter-play of winds and ocean currents giving rise to zones and pockets of ex-treme dessication. In one region in the southern hemisphere, two highly contrasting, wind currents, the Antarctic Wind Current sweep-ing north and hitting the warmer, Pacific Wind Current moving east-ward, result in the formation of fog-laden clouds. This moist air, thus warmed, can pick up greater moisture but not enough to make rain fall, the moisture-laden winds meanwhile rolling inland. The Atacama Desert in South America is one of these seacoast deserts, with only a half-inch of rainfall a year—the driest desert in the world.

Deserts circle the world mainly in two great bands above and below the equator. Frequently they are found in the western portions of con-tinents where winds moving from west to east sweep away the cloud cover. There are some deserts, however, in cold climates. Much of the arctic tundra is really a cold desert.

Our Great American Desert is characterized by five types of deserts: the Great Basin Desert, the largest in area and marked by the sagebrush and located mostly in Utah and Nevada; the Mohave Desert of lower California and southwestern Arizona and identified generally by the Joshua tree; the Painted Desert of northeastern Arizona and northwestern New Mexico; the Chihuahuan Desert in Southern New Mexico and northeastern Mexico and represented by the yucca; and the Sonoran Desert of southern Arizona and the province of Sonora Mexico and typified by the giant saguaro cactus.

I have chosen to describe the Sonoran Desert not because it is the most representative of our deserts but because it is a fascinating desert and one that I know best.

To walk in the Sonoran on a bright morning after a short night rain is like walking into some strange mystical garden. Everywhere

there is a sense of awakening. The sweet smell of sage fills your nostrils. All around, the architecture of the earth's surface is visible—purple mountains rising sharply from pancake flats, dry stream beds shining white in the cliffs, and still moist sands making up small and big aprons where rivulets and stream beds flatten out onto the plain.

Water, the traveler quickly becomes aware, is the working tool of the desert. Wind follows a close second. Even though rain comes rarely, it leaves its mark. When it does come, it comes in cloudbursts, filling the streams, spilling over cliffs, loosening great sheets of flood water down the canyons. For a few hours it bites, scours, and chisels away granite and schist, carrying heavy loads of abrasive sand to the valley floor. The rains that do occur, however, are not the drenching downpours of the east. It is only because there is so little absorbent cover and much rapid run-off that storms seem more devastating.

To witness the massive exodus of water down a steep canyon following a sudden downpour is to see an awesome spectacle in nature. So overpowering is the sight, so deafening the roar, that one's senses become a little numb. The magnitude and power of a deluge in a big canyon, with precipitous, vise-like walls, is just short of unbelievable: first there is a tugging wind which tries to sweep you into the canyon; then there is the rumble of great boulders as they roll downstream like huge marbles. Other rocks shake, twist, and grind out potholes in the granite; smaller rocks, the size of apples and grapefruit, careen down the bouncing water as if riding some violent escalator. There is a continued deafening roar, like Niagara.

Only after the flood subsides and the canyon stream-bed becomes dry again do you know the sculptural and architectural power of the water that once was there. In the White Tanks area near Phoenix, Arizona, one can scale chalk-like walls of pure granite to see superb silos of stone chiseled out of a magnificent canyon—white tanks of solid rock drilled out of the face of a mountain.

When the waters sweep out of the desert mountains they are suddenly checked by the valley floors, lose their sand and sediment and spread gentle alluvial fans in many directions. Beyond these aprons the slower waters carry the finer sand and silt, filling the valleys with layer after layer of fine soil. So deep are some of the valleys in silt-laden soil that well drillers find clays and loams more than 300 feet below the surface. Some valleys have been found to have as much as 3,000 feet of sediment.

Desert streams seldom reach the sea. At best they may end up as temporary, shallow lakes or playas, soon to disappear in the parched earth, leaving a glaze of mud that soon bakes hard as pottery clay, only to shrivel up again and break up into millions of oddly-shaped fragments. Because of soil hardness and the fact that alkaline salts are continually added, few plants grow in these dried-up lake beds. Most of the plants that flourish are confined to the edges and to the rising slopes of the Lower Sonoran Desert zone. Here one finds plant life in surprising abundance and, in places, in almost unbelievable patterns. So uniformly are the plants spaced that the observer is reminded of a plant nursery—each salt-bush just so far apart from the next, each thoroughly weeded, and clear, roomy pathways between the plants. No landscape gardener could do a better job and still have the plants look natural.

In the Sonoran there is a striking change in the climate as one moves up and down the slopes of ridges and mountains. There is a five degree change in average temperature with each 1,000 feet of elevation. This phenomenon was first observed in the San Francisco Peaks range of northern Arizona by C. Hart Merriam and gave rise to the *life zone* theory now widely accepted by naturalists and ecologists.

In travelling northward across the Americas from the equator to the arctic, one may easily see seven major life zones—belts of plant and animal life that have certain distinct characteristics. These have been given descriptive names representative of the land areas in which they reach their greatest development. Around the equator is the *Tropical* life zone. Further northward is the *Lower Sonoran,* followed by *Upper Sonoran.* Then comes the *Transition,* followed by the *Canadian, Hudsonian* and *Arctic.* In the Sonoran Desert the visitor in one afternoon can travel through three of these life zones—Lower Sonoran, Upper Sonoran, and the Transition. A little further northward, up the slopes of the higher mountains, he can find the remaining three: Hudsonian, Arctic-alpine, and Tundra. The visitor who will take time to see each of these vegetative zones will be repaid well by what he sees. Nowhere else in the world is the change in flora or fauna so striking.

One of the interesting things about the Lower Sonoran Desert is its great diversity of plant and animal life. One never ceases to wonder why this is so—why so many species of xerophytic plants, like the cacti and sages, live here. Why do so many birds and reptiles and insects choose to make the desert their home? In an environment which is essentially harsh, abundant life seems like a paradox. Perhaps this is one of those unexplainable mysteries which make the world of the desert so fascinating.

Much of the overall pale-green cast of the landscape one sees in the desert comes from the foothill paloverde tree. It is easily recognized by the pale yellow green bark of its trunk and branches which carry on the normal function of leaves. Thus, during periods of drought, the paloverde can drop its leaves to reduce loss of moisture without discontinuing its normal life processes.

The common olive-green shrub closely associated with the paloverde is the creosote bush, one of the most abundant and successful of all desert shrubs. It is native to all the deserts of the southwestern United States and northern Mexico. Its success as a desert shrub is due to its highly efficient root system. A wide-spreading network of shallow roots takes advantage of the moisture provided by infrequent rains while long taproots penetrate deep into the earth to reach more dependable deep water.

The mesquite (pronounced muskeet), a wide-ranging scrubby tree with dark gray, almost black bark, depends almost entirely on deep taproots for its moisture. The beans of this legume which appear in great abundance during the summer months were a staple food of the southwestern Indians.

The saguaro forest supports a surprising number and variety of wildlife. These include such unusual creatures as the gila monster, the only poisonous lizard found in the United States, diamondback rattler,

horned toad, tarantula, the kangaroo rat which chemically manufactures its water from a diet of dry seeds, and the collared peccary or javelina which thrives on its diet of needle-spined pads of the prickly pear cactus. Some animals, like the desert mule deer, must depend on widely scattered springs and water holes for their moisture, but most desert animals survive primarily upon the moisture contained in their food.

The gila woodpecker and gilded flicker are the "real estate developers" of saguaro land. They cut out the nesting holes which one sees in the larger saguaros. A saguaro has the remarkable ability to seal a wound quickly with a thin layer of callus tissue, thereby eliminating the loss of precious moisture. The sealing of the wound against infection takes less than 30 minutes. Thus, in a short time, the woodpecker is provided with a weather proof "air conditioned apartment." In succeeding years these apartments are often taken over by other birds such as the sparrow sized elf owl, screech owl, purple martin, sparrow hawk, and flycatcher. Here then lies an intricate interrelationship between the saguaro, woodpecker and elf owl.

The saguaro has been called a "bird cafeteria." Actually it represents a whole community of complex animal life, providing housing and food for a wide range of forms from insects to small rodents. Cactus blossoms supply a feast of nectar as well as an abundance of insect food. Especially conspicuous among the diners is the white-winged dove. Early arrivals are on hand to feed on the nectar of the first blossoms, followed by an ever-increasing number of other animals as blooms become more abundant in May.

The real banquet, however, comes with the ripening of the fruits in June and July. The fruits, weighing about a quarter of a pound each, split open like a half-peeled banana displaying a content that suggests blackberry jam. The sweet, juicy pulp contains thousands of tiny saguaro seeds. This is a time of feasting not only for the doves, thrashers, cactus wrens, and other birds, but for a host of ground-dwelling animals such as skunk, raccoon, kit fox and many rodents.

At the time of the establishment of the Saguaro National Monument in 1933, near Tucson, the cactus forest was considered to be the finest stand of adult saguaros anywhere in the country. Today the picture is vastly changed. The saguaros now seen are but a remnant of the original forest. Many dead but standing skeletons silhouette the landscape. Most of them, however, are now a bundle of dried sticks lying prostrate on the desert floor, victims of wind, frost, disease, and the heavy encroachment of humans upon the desert.

While frost and other natural forces have taken a heavy toll of big saguaros, this alone does not explain its plight and possible disappearance. It is reasonable to expect that old plants will weaken and die, and that younger plants will in turn take their place. But younger plants are hard to find and this may doom the saguaro by the end of the present century.

Why is this happening? Why is no one doing anything about it? Is there any hope for the saguaros? For answers to these questions one must go back 100 years to the time when the larger saguaros were tiny seedlings hidden under fallen branches of the paloverde and the mesquite. This was a thriving saguaro forest with old, middleaged, young, and, most important, infant plants. Sometime during recent decades, however, changes began taking place which changed the vegetation from a "thriving forest" to a "surviving forest." Exactly what these changes were no one can say for certain. It is a fact that this was a time when great herds of cattle were turned loose to fatten on the grasses blanketing the desert. When hundreds of thousands of hungry mouths were turned loose, plus the trampling by hoofed feet, the delicate saguaro seedlings could not survive. With over-grazing came also drought, the lowering of the water table, and much gully erosion. When the valley forests and meadows were gone, the cattle were moved to the slopes. Here the destruction has continued. It seems incredible that even today, except for a small fenced area, that cattle grazing is still permitted in this delicately-balanced land.

Yet with all of its destructive effects, grazing alone cannot be held totally responsible for the saguaro's plight. Other changes have taken place: pumping from wells has lowered the level of underground water, air pollution has come with the arrival of industry and thousands of new residents have moved into the Tucson Valley. The most significant change, however, may be in the climate itself. Average temperatures throughout the Southwest have slowly increased since the beginning of the century. The increase is slight by present-day standards—only about three degrees. Yet for delicately adjusted plants growing at the extreme limit of their range, such a change is a "life and death" matter. The warmer temperatures have allowed the saguaros to increase at higher elevations. However, one of the peculiar consequences of the change in climate is that frost has taken a large toll of the young in this area. On calm winter nights cold heavy air drains toward the valleys, while lighter warm air rises and spreads out in a layer on top of the colder air. As a result of this phenomenon called "temperature inversion," prolonged frosts sometimes occur at low elevations while warmer temperatures prevail on the higher slopes.

Undoubtedly, the change in climate has altered conditions affecting germination and survival of saguaro seedlings. The seeds of this big cactus normally germinate during the period of summer rains in July, August, and September. Both temperature and moisture needs are so critical that a slight change in either condition can virtually prevent establishment of young plants.

When an occasional seedling becomes established it faces a severe test during the hot, dry months of May and June. Because of its small size, the average seedling seldom survives the prolonged drought which commonly occurs in late spring and early summer. Those plants which struggle without benefit of shade from other plants are doomed to wither in the burning sun. Rodents, too, play a part in the destruction of seedlings. Unless concealed by rocks or vegetation, young saguaros are eagerly consumed by prolific ground squirrels and woodrats. The fate of the saguaro therefore hinges also on the health of its many plant neighbors who make up the cactus forest community.

In recounting the case of the stricken saguaro one cannot overlook the fate of its neighbors. Less conspicuous but equally dramatic changes are taking place with other members of the saguaro community. The foothill paloverde, Sonoran jumping cholla and others seem to be losing their place too. A few species, however, such as the creosote bush and prickly pear seem to be on the increase. Other species, too, are affected, but definite conclusions as to status must wait for the answers which only careful studies and time can provide.

The disappearance of the saguaro, while no longer a total mystery, cannot be explained in one or two simple causes. The saguaro is a sensitive, delicate, precisely-adjusted plant whose survival hinges on a whole series of combined effects in a complicated environment. Like a complex machine with all of its parts invisibly linked, every part of its environment relates to the rest. No part may be changed without, somehow, in some way, affecting all of the rest. This is the great law of life, the intricate interplay between plants and animals and man, between weather and climate and the physical earth itself—a law that man must appreciate or else he will hasten the demise of the saguaro and very possibly even himself.

ALPINE BIOME— HIGH ISLANDS IN THE SKY

HIGH AND WINDSWEPT. COLD. TREELESS. BREATHLESS. MOUNTAIN peaks and mountain meadows. Desolate islands in the sky. All these, and more, characterize the arctic-alpine strongholds of our land. This is the country you see far away above the timberline, snow-covered during the cold weather months and purplish, gray and bleak in the summer, a wild and hostile environment but nonetheless a place of extraordinary happenings and scenic splendor.

Little known and even less understood, the alpine island zone is really a restricted area of arctic tundra pulled down into temperate latitudes—a region occurring at correspondingly higher altitudes as one moves away from the polar regions.

Most of my visits to arctic-alpine regions in the United States have resulted from my contacts with a forester-wildlifer friend, Con Tolman, of Denver. Con has known this high country intimately and lives and works in a state which contains more arctic-alpine land than any other, save perhaps Alaska. Colorado has more than 40 peaks which tower above 14,000 feet in the Rocky Mountain sky.

My first journey into the high, standing-up country took place one autumn day in the Rocky Mountain National Park. We had saddled up with three good mountain horses and a pack mule and soon were bound for a distant alpine lake high above timberline. Con was on the lead horse and set a steady pace. After hours of climbing mountainsides and cliffs, he called for a halt.

"We're about eleven thousand feet now," he announced, "and from here on in it's going to be tough going. We'd better take it easy."

What he meant was that the trail was now going to be sharply upward, at times non-existent, and we'd be having lots of hard climbing.

We rested our horses frequently but the thin air was beginning to tell on them. The human thing to do was to dismount and walk. And no sooner had we done so when I began to feel a noticeable sharp pinching in my lungs—rarified air indeed. We came to a rimrock shelf and gazed down and across a vast and stupendous land.

We climbed another thousand feet and watched the Engelmann spruce give way to smaller and smaller trees. Presently a narrow precipice appeared and the trail led over it. "Just wide enough for a bighorn ram," Con said. So we mounted our horses and rode across, peering down into a deep awesome canyon. Shivers rolled over my spine. When we were finally safely across, I breathed again and felt immeasurably relieved. Then the trail just gave out. Now we met only boulders and isolated spruces and downfalls. Everything was upward. The mountain pass we were searching for was still a thousand feet up. Now it was each one for himself. When we finally scrambled onto a dizzy precipice, rocks and gravel rolling loose behind us, we paused like Indians on a lookout. The view was an indescribable panorama—towering rocky peaks, a vast blanket of greenery on three sides, and a magnificent valley of fir, spruce and aspen below us. We could hear the distant roar of plummeting water as it tumbled invisibly down through some hidden canyon.

We clambered upward toward a still higher mountain top and then halted to catch our breath. Here we gazed almost straight down into a basin of reflected shimmering watery beauty—our alpine lake. I took several more painful breaths, and each time a surge of emotion swept through me like when one stands up for the magnificent *Hallelujah* chorus in the Messiah. We remained transfixed by the grandeur —a time not for words but thought and subconscious enjoyment.

Suddenly, at this moment of great feeling, a sharp crack reverberated through the alpine country. Con's experienced ears and eyes picked it up instantly, "Rams! They're bighorns, across that alpine valley, on that rocky precipice."

My binoculars picked them up quickly. They were big with massive heads and they were squared off for another encounter. In a brief moment they pawed the rocks, heads low, eyeing each other at ten yards. Then they bolted toward each other and met bone against bone with another resounding crack. It was incredible. How could these 300-pound male bighorn sheep take such punishment. But the battle was over for the moment, for the rams sensed our presence and disappeared over the cliff.

Bighorns don't approach easily, so we had a treat of a lifetime. White sheep, called Dall sheep, are more easily approached. An acquaintance of mine, Les Blacklock, a noted still photographer, told me how he approached the Dalls in the Yukon alpine country. "I just slowly follow them and soon get accepted as part of the landscape," he said. And he has good pictures to prove it.

Slowly our full sensibilities returned. One by one we picked our way down a series of steep rocky inclines and finally came to the lake

—a cirque at the foot of a barren, towering peak. Without a doubt this was one of the most beautiful mountain jewels of water I had ever seen.

High mountain tops are such places and do deep things to a man.

So enriching was this experience that I must join the chorus of many others who believe that at some point in one's life one should climb a mountain. Like seashores and deserts, mountains make a man look up into the clouds, force him to squint into the sun and ponder. They make him slow down, become himself again, and bring him face to face with his Creator.

Viewpoint and values are matters of perspective. A mountain top gives a man a wider view of things, including himself. Today many men equate progress with high speed superhighways, tall buildings, and the fullness of the refrigerator. They feel that progress entails the gradual elimination of everything that nature has given us and its substitution by the material things that man has made. They fail to see that just beyond the expressway that cuts the city's heartland in two there is dire poverty, that around the expensive high-rise apartments there is no grass to walk on, no trees to leaf out in the spring. Thus it seems to me that if men would get out of their conveyances and walk even a trifle, they would soon see how shallow our illusion of progress really is. A mountain top, climbed high on foot, surely affords the viewer a fresher view of himself and his spaceship Earth.

One can admire mountain tops, then, for these and many other reasons. They are, for one, among the few remaining natural worlds where the sojourner can come face to face with nature and feel his total self again. I have sojourned in my day to many mountains—high places in the wooded east, in the south, in the great west, in British Columbia, Alaska, the Andes—and have found all high places clarifying in mind and uplifting in spirit. Mountains have taught me much, that while we need good roads and great superhighways, our people also need something more: the quiet backwoods, the foot trail to the hemlock glen, the high waterfall, the undisturbed rimrocks and mesas and the treeless greenery of high meadows.

The arctic-alpine country is small in area compared to the arctic tundra of the north and so it seems reasonable to say that these precious wild places should be safeguarded at all costs. The alpine region of western North America is the home of pikas, marmots, mountain goat (not a goat at all but an antelope related to the European chamois), mountain sheep, Dall sheep (in Northern Canada and Alaska), and elk. The sheep and elk spend their summers on the high alpine meadows and in the timberline country of the high slopes. They winter in the lower slopes above the valleys where there is food. The marmot, a type of mountain woodchuck, hibernates over winter, while the pika braves the cold and cuts grass and piles it in tiny bundles to dry for the winter.

The vole and pocket gopher remain under the ground and snow during cold weather, coming up only on warmer days. The pocket gopher, like the prairie dog of the plains, is important for his activities change the pattern of alpine vegetation. In winter these rodents tunnel a good deal and kill the sedge and forbs by eating the roots. When these plants die, others take over the wind-blown gravelly soil. Such pioneering plants are also utilized by the gopher. These rodents increase, the bunch grass comes back in, and organic material accumulates again. Slowly the alpine vegetation recovers, and when it does the gopher population becomes stable. This healing process may take more than 50 years, for vegetative change is very slow on the arctic-alpine tundra.

Alpine strongholds contain a good representation of insect life. Mosquitoes, gnats and large flies are scarce, but springtails, beetles, grasshoppers, and butterflies are common. The ever-present winds, however, force the butterflies to stay close to the ground; other insects have short wings or no wings at all. Insect development is slow; some butterflies may take two years to mature and grasshoppers three.

A major problem for mammals of the alpine tundra is low oxygen pressure. Birds with higher metabolism obviously are able to live at high altitudes where oxygen pressure is low, but mammals that wander into high places, unless they live there permanently and become adapted to rarefied air, have a difficult time breathing. Normal air pressure for most mammalian life is 14.7 pounds per square inch. At high alpine elevations this pressure often drops to 10 pounds at 10,000 feet and is even lower higher up; at 18,000 feet, air pressure is reduced by one-half. In such a rarefied atmosphere the mammal, including man, gasps for breath because of insufficient oxygen and often succumbs. A few mammals, like the elk, can adapt themselves to high altitudes by increasing the heart beat and the rate of respiration. Some elk herds spend their entire lifetime at timberline and above. Mammals permanently adapted to high altitudes, like the mountain goat and bighorn sheep, have blood richer in red cells and hemoglobin.

Unique among arctic-alpine mountain tops of the West where the alpine biome is most pronounced is Mt. Evans in Colorado. It is nowhere nearly as well known as Pike's Peak but in the judgment of many naturalists, ecologists, and travelers it is a much more fascinating mountain. It is much more rugged than Pike's Peak, has more alpine tundra above timberline, and is higher. Moreover one can drive almost to the very top, to 14,200 feet above sea level. This makes Evans the highest mountain accessible by auto in all of North America, in fact, in the entire world.

But Evans is not an easy climb. Some effort and a measure of risk are required to see it. There are innumerable switchbacks and dangerous drop-offs. The road to its top is open only after July 4 and closes soon after Labor Day. Then the mountain belongs to nature, and the few rugged adventurers who seek its pleasures and hardships.

I've been on Evans several times but only once was the auto road negotiable to the very top. It was late August, a Monday, when Con Tolman suggested a trip to the top of Mt. Evans. Joining Con and me, were Helen, Con's wife, and their 12-year-old son Tom, and my 14-year-old daughter, Nancy.

When we rolled into the quaint mountain community of Golden, it was mid-morning, hot but brisk, and already the leaves of the cottonwoods and aspen were beginning to show tinges of yellow.

We stopped at a filling station and, after checking the map, Con pointed: "That's Evans up there. See the bare summit beyond that first mountain? That's where we'll be heading."

We hit the road and turned left at a junction just outside of town. "From here on," Con said, "we'll be on the Evans road. You'll enjoy seeing the change in the vegetation."

The elevation around Golden is some 5,675 feet. This is aspen country and what remains of the western pine or ponderosa forest type. As we moved above this line of scattered pines the character of the vegetation changed sharply, the transition being toward aspen balds and patches of Douglas-fir. The Douglas-fir here is at its easternmost range and gets thicker and larger as one goes westward. It reaches its finest composition in the cool, moist Pacific coast ranges where, in some instances, as in British Columbia, it reaches a girth of ten or more feet and a height of 275 feet. (In the McMillan Park on Vancouver Island, at the base of Mt. Arrowsmith, I measured a Douglas-fir that was 24 feet in circumference around its base).

On the eastern slope of Colorado, the *Pseudotsuga menziesii,* as the foresters call the Douglas-fir, intermingles with the lodgepole pine and Englemann and blue spruce. The lodgepole is a remarkable tree, true to its name for, in pure, even-aged stands, no pine is straighter or more uniform in appearance. It makes one think of how easy it would be to make a log cabin out of its clean, straight stems—and many a cabin or lodge, of course, is built of them.

As we climbed to the nine and ten thousand foot levels, the car coughed frequently and at times stalled. The carburetor was not set properly for high altitudes. Now the lovely, lance-shaped Englemann spruce of the higher altitudes began to put in an appearance. The Englemann is one of our most beautiful spruces and nowhere is it more spire-shaped or lovelier than on the high slopes of the Rockies. At the ten and eleven thousand foot levels the Englemann slowly gives way to open barrens and strange forms of scattered bristlecone pines. Now it was obvious that we were at timberline—the edge of tree growth. Above, for the next two thousand feet, it was all alpine country. The car stalled at every point where we stopped to take pictures. The country is now typical arctic-alpine tundra. So precipitous are the

dropoffs that Tom and Nancy hesitated to look out the window. Helen sat transfixed in the back seat but Con and I in the front were enjoying every moment of it.

We stopped at a switchback where a single, last stand of the bristlecone pine gave way to the tundra. I wanted more pictures and a chance to examine the trees. They certainly were odd.

The bristlecone pine *(Pinus aristata)* is an interesting but little known pine. It is a member of the foxtail pines, a small group of alpine trees, two of which are found in the western United States. The name *foxtail* is due to the bushy nature of the young branches of these pines, much like the bushy tail of a fox.

I have seen the five-needled bristlecone in several places in the central and south Rocky Mountain region and everywhere found it intriguing. It ranges from the high country of the Nevada-California border eastward at or near timberline in Nevada, Utah, Colorado, northern Arizona, and northern New Mexico.

One cannot stop and study these incredible trees without a strong feeling of admiration. Twisted, gnarled, they bend and hug the fierce landscape in beaten form, for their life at these altitudes is beset by savage winds, cold and ice and snow, and in summer by burning heat and desiccation.

Not so many years ago it was thought that the title of the oldest living thing in the world must go to the redwoods of California. Now comes evidence that this is not so. Today there is much proof that the title must pass—or rather should always have passed—to the bristle-cone pine. The discovery was made by a dendrochronologist, the late Dr. Edmund Schulman, who, as associate professor in the Tree Ring Laboratory of the University of Arizona, announced that bristlecone pines were over 4,000 years old.

The most amazing of the bristlecones survive in grotesque form on the high arid slopes of the White Mountains in eastern California near the town of Bishop, some 60 miles southeast of Yosemite National Park. Ted Schlapfur and Bill Huber of the U. S. Forest Service first told me about the area and I became determined to visit it one day. I have since seen these aged, wind-polished, remarkable trees and they are a spectacular sight. I dare say that only a few foresters and naturalists and some of the more adventurous tourists have seen them. Several trees in particular are noteworthy.

One ravaged, twisted old monarch is Pine Alpha—more than 4,000 years old. Though largely dead, like most trees since only the sapwood is alive, it still clings courageously to life and even produces viable seeds. Two outstanding groves in the 28,000-acre Ancient Bristlecone Forest are the Schulman Grove at 10,000 feet and Patriarch Grove at 12,000 feet. The latter has some superlative trees, like the baby Patriarch which is 1800 years old and has a 37 foot circumference at its

base and is the largest tree in the forest. The Schulman Grove has the grandfather of all trees—Methuselah, age 4600 years, and the oldest living thing in the world.

As we moved ever upward beyond the bristlecone pine fringe on Mt. Evans, the alpine meadows showed up below the cirques. Here, for the first time, I felt as if I were on the true alpine tundra.

One of the dwarfed plants which the alpinist sees at these heights is the leathery-leaved arctic willow. This ground-hugging plant in late August turns russet brown and is striking on the treeless landscape. This same *Salix reticulata,* in contrast, is found close to sea level on the sub-arctic flats of Canada, especially around Churchill, along Hudson Bay.

Arctic wildflowers bloom from late May to early September and at times turn the high country into a floral carpet. Most common of the Colorado alpine wildflowers are: alpine avens, Queen's crown, western paintbrush, alpine forget-me-not, Fendler's sandwort, and King's crown. There is also the arctic gentian, least lewisia, American bistort, deer clover, greenleaf chiming bells, alpine clover, moss campion, bush cinquefoil and alpine bluebells. In places one can see silky phacelia, globe flower, alplily, twinflower sandwort, twisted-pod draba and the fairy primrose. In some spots the alpine androsace, alpine sandwort, and sky pilot are evident, as are Queen's crown (red plant in the fall), graylocks actinea, and Jacob's ladder. Others often seen are tufted phlox, yellow saxifrage, marsh marigold (alpine), yellow stonecrop, and the alpine anemone; also the snow buttercups, alpine wallflower, stemless wooly actinea, the glacier lily—all help make up the alpine magic carpet.

Above 12,000 feet, Mt. Evans is a mixture of rock, rock formations, cirques and alpine lakes. Steep grassy areas in places mark the typical tundra of the far north. Here in the awesome, high altitude country persists a variety of biota. Over the ground runs the strange ptarmigan and high over the cliffs and crags circles the occasional raven and falcon. At times the golden eagle appears.

The top of Evans is negotiated by a series of sharp switchbacks.

One can look down across the tundra into cirques and valleys a thousand or more feet below. This is "top of the world country", beautiful and scenically spectacular. When one finally reaches the parking lot at the top, the elevation, 14,120 feet, and the cold, rarefied air are quick to tell you this is high, high country.

The summit of Evans is still another 300 feet up a steep, rocky peak. If you're game, it's a fifteen to twenty minute hike with pinching lungs along a safe trail to the top. To stand on top of the world one must negotiate several jagged rocks with one particularly forbidding. But the more adventurous scramble onto it and then slowly raise up to full height.

The view is overpowering. So bone-chilling is the sight from this topmost rock that it makes one a little dizzy. Few people chance this rock because the view is so frightening, but young Tom and I just had to make it.

As I looked down into the great chasms and canyons below, I felt immensely chilled inside. The wind was gentle but the temperature was in the low forties. But this was not the reason. For half a century I had lived but never had I experienced such amazing heights before—how remarkable and entrancing an adventure. It was like seeing Niagara Falls for the first time. It was strongly reminiscent of a chill of a spring night when a strange nature orchestra played in the great Okefenokee swamp.

One does not climb a very high mountain often in his life and the feeling is new and deep and soul-satisfying.

Alpine mountain tops also occur in the East. Mount Katahdin in Maine has alpine conditions. So does even Mt. Desert Island, a relatively low mountain at the coast, in Acadia National Park. In New Hampshire most of the higher peaks in the White Mountains show tundra characteristics above 4500 feet. Mount Washington, of course, has remarkable tundra growth all over its summit. Here is another fascinating mountain and one can drive all the way to its summit during warmer months. In the Green Mountains of Vermont alpine conditions prevail on most mountain tops. The Adirondacks too have their alpine strongholds in the sky, notably Mt. Marcy and Whiteface Mountain. In southern Quebec, tundra conditions are seen on Mt. Saint Hilaire, a low mountain. The further north one travels the more he sees arctic-alpine country at lower elevations. Finally, along Hudson Bay, the alpine conditions give way to tundra at sea level.

The alpine strongholds and the arctic tundra have much in common. Both have low temperatures and low precipitation. Both display short growing seasons. Both possess a frost-molded landscape and plant species whose growth form is stunted and whose growth rate is slow. The arctic tundra has a permafrost layer; the alpine tundra rarely has it. Arctic plants require longer periods of daylight than alpine plants and reproduce vegetatively, while alpine plants propagate themselves by seedlings. Over much of the Arctic, the dominant vegetation is cottongrass, sedge, and dwarf heaths. In the alpine tundra, cushion and mat-forming plants which are able to withstand buffeting by the wind, dominate the exposed sites, while cottongrass and other tundra plants are confined to protected sites. At the tree line lies the krumholtz, a land of stunted, wind-shaped trees, a growth form that may be genetically determined. Animal life in the arctic tundra, except for the caribou and the pipit, is distinct from that of the alpine and is circumpolar in distribution. White is the dominant color of tundra birds and mammals, especially in winter; white grays and browns predominate in alpine lands. For mammals of the alpine tundra a major problem is low oxygen pressure, a situation that animals of the arctic tundra generally do not face. The tundra region, arctic and alpine, is a rigorous environment for plants and animals, but, in spite of it, the tundra, contrary to its implied barrenness, is a land enormously rich in life—if not in variety, then in seasonal abundance.

Arctic-alpine strongholds are vanishing wilds. Too many have already disappeared, yielded to ski lodges, overlooks, restaurants, motels. Surely these unusual and highly fragile places of nature deserve a better fate. Perhaps a moratorium against the further development of pristine mountain tops has come of age.

Saga of a Mountain Top Bird

Mountain tops above timberline are islands of retreat for many living things. Just as remnant swamps are sanctuaries for rare and disappearing plants and animals, so too the tops of mountains often provide the last refuge for certain wild creatures. Perhaps the most classic example of a threatened species now being crowded into a single mountain sanctuary is the California condor. The survival story of this bird on the North American continent, although perhaps less publicized than the whooping crane, is nonetheless dramatic and noteworthy. But while the whooper's chances of survival seem fairly promising today, the outlook for the condor is not bright.

An ungainly bird with a wingspread of nine to eleven feet, the California condor was once widely distributed along the coastal Pacific ranges from the Columbia River to northern Lower California and eastward to Arizona. In recent years, however, man's activities have so harassed this bird that now its range is restricted to a limited mountain range in the Los Padres National Forest, north of Los Angeles.

Feeding mostly on carrion but ranging extensively for food up and down the valleys from its mountain haunts, the condor, a vulture, had been so maligned by gunners that in the 1940's its numbers were drastically reduced. A survey at that time by the National Audubon Society revealed only some 60 birds—the entire population of the species. This resulted in a special refuge being set up in the national forest in the hope that the dwindling condors could be preserved.

Twenty years later the Society again initiated a survey to determine the bird's status. On a warm day in November 1964, in Tucson, Arizona, the Society's convention members received the distressing news that only about 40 of the birds remained, a drop of more than 30 percent in 20 years.

This second bird count grew out of an investigation financed by the National Geographic Society and was conducted during 1962-1964 by Ian and Eben McMillan, brothers, under the scientific direction of Dr. Alden H. Miller, noted ornithologist and director of the Museum of Vertebrate Zoology at the University of California, Berkeley.

Dr. Miller and the McMillans found the condors losing ground. They attributed the decline principally to one factor: reckless shooting. The wide-ranging adult birds were being shot by irresponsible or ignorant gunners faster than the breeding pairs could replace their losses.

Nine cases of shooting of condors in a four-year period were reported. At least five of the events resulted in dead or injured condors, and represented but a fraction of the total of such cases occurring.

It was believed, however, that the downward trend could be reversed if the illegal killing could be halted or at least nearly eliminated. Dr. Miller said the species was "viable," and that the number of immature birds in the current population showed that the condor was successfully bringing off young, although at a naturally slow rate of reproduction. A breeding pair normally lays only one egg every two years.

By characteristic plumage markings that show when the birds soar overhead, trained observers can distinguish young condors up to five years of age. Dr. Miller and the McMillans found at least ten birds under six years of age.

The researchers stressed the necessity of absolute freedom from human intrusion, particularly in the area of rugged cliffs and canyons where the condors nest. The sensitive birds have a tendency to abandon either egg or young if they even see a person within the vicinity of their nest.

The very high sensitivity of the species to human disturbance was established as scientific fact by Dr. Carl B. Koford, who studied the biology of the condors under Dr. Miller's supervision in the late 1940's. It was the Koford study that resulted in the previous estimate of a population of about 60 birds.

"We are convinced the condor can survive," Dr. Miller declared. "We decry any defeatist attitudes in this regard. But make no mistake, old procedures must be greatly bolstered, new dangers warded off, and new practices vigorously pursued! Enforcement of the laws that protect the condors and other large, soaring birds with which they may be confused should have high priority."

Dr. Miller also said the National Audubon Society itself should employ a full-time condor warden to supplement the work of a Forest Service patrolman whose salary, in the past and now, is partially contributed by the Society.

Dr. Miller and the McMillans also urged intensive education by the Society, the U.S. Forest Service, and the State Fish and Game Department, directed at key groups and the general public. Such efforts were deemed essential to win the support and cooperation of both official agencies and private citizens in the conservation effort.

The research team concluded that a scarcity of food was not a problem for the condors, as some persons have conjectured. The McMillans, who are themselves ranchers as well as naturalists, estimated that "9,854 carcasses of livestock and deer are available annually in the foraging range of the condor and there is no seasonal period when food is scarce."

The Sespe Wildlife Refuge of 35,000 acres within the Los Padres National Forest was established in 1951 by order of the Secretary of Interior. The prime purpose was to safeguard the condor breeding and roosting areas. Dr. Miller and the McMillans indicated, however, that this area should be augmented by buffer zones and wilderness areas from which guns would be excluded.

Other recommendations were that mass recreation should be ruled out in the area and that there should be no yielding to development of a dam and a lake in the region inhabited by the condor. New roads opening up sections of the national forest in the range of the condor should be so located and designed as to avoid or minimize disruption to the safe use of the area by condors.

It was also argued that rodent-poisoning agencies should devise different methods and timing of activities to minimize the threat to condors. The team cited circumstantial evidence of the death of some condors through eating poisoned rodents killed by the chemical known as "compound 1080," a material commonly used by predator and rodent control agents. They said research should be done on turkey vultures to determine the effect of different dosage levels of 1080 on the general health of such vultures.

In 1967 the Society appointed John Bornaman as condor naturalist and warden and the progress of the condors has been watched closely. Bornaman has great hope that the condors can be saved. The keys to survival are the preservation of its vital habitat and the preservation and perpetuity of a vital wild breeding stock. If these fail, the condor is doomed. So the education and enlightenment of the public to the condor plight is essential.

According to Roland C. Clement, vice president of the National Audubon Society and a noted biologist who has been following the predicament of the condor closely for many years, the hope for this bird is not bright. Man must seriously amend his activities, he thinks, if the condor is to be saved.

The Los Padres mountain tops and others, then, are needed not only for the physical, esthetic, and spiritual values they furnish man but also for the vital habitat they provide for rare forms of wildlife. Like other delicately balanced biomes, such as swamps, marshes and grassland, they are indispensable to both humans and wildlife. For the casual naturalist or visiting outdoorsman who may never climb Mount McKinley or see the California condor in its high country retreat, there is comfort in the knowledge that the mountains are there, that they can be climbed and enjoyed if one wishes. And just the mere thought that a rare bird still lives on a mountain seems reason enough to leave such places undisturbed. While he is of a minority, democracy demands that even the wishes of his minority group be respected, lest by ignoring them we endanger the great good of the majority.

THE GREAT HUDSONIAN WILDERNESS

NORTH OF THE CONTINENTAL LIMITS OF MUCH OF THE UNITED STATES, across the broad sweep of southern and central Canada, with limited sections dipping into the mountainous states, lies a wide expanse of evergreen trees second to none in the world. From eastern Newfoundland and southern Labrador the green mantle unfolds, stretching westward to the southern shores of Hudson Bay, then on northwestward to the cold waters of the Arctic Sea. And that is not all. From this point it still rolls on across northern Yukon and far into Alaska. Then it sweeps southward across British Columbia and drops south into Washington, Oregon, and on into California. Then it swings eastward across northern Idaho, Montana, and extends across the northern Lake States and finally into southern Ontario and Quebec— a unique green world of spruces and firs, 5,000 miles long and 1,000 miles wide.

This is the mighty Hudsonian forest, a wilderness so vast and in places so remote as to stagger one's imagination. No other wilderness of evergreen trees in the entire world can match it for vastness and wild beauty.

The Hudsonian wilderness has a cool forest climate which at times goes by the names of boreal forest or the North Woods. In its upper reaches its evergreen trees dwindle to sparse and stunted spruces known, from the Russians, as *taiga*.

The climate of this vast and delightful forest system is severe with temperatures going to the extremes in the winter. Even in the summer the days and nights are cool. The climate is quite similar to the alpine country with somewhat less moisture, generally colder temperatures, and less daylight and wind.

The soils of the Hudsonian are dark with much humus which, again from the Russian, are called *podzol* soils or *chernozems*. The surface layer is made up of needles, twigs, bark, sticks and other vegetative materials which decompose very slowly. Under such conditions much humus and, eventually, peat develops. In warmer climes the soils have a higher temperature, and decomposition of organic matter by bacteria is more rapid. In most parts of the Canadian prairie provinces these soils are extremely fertile. On new lands the farmers need only clear the land of the bush and plant wheat. No artificial fertilizers are required, in fact none may be needed for decades. On the Alberta black-chernozem farmlands, northwest of Edmonton, wheat farmers have yet to resort to phosphates. So rich are these podzols that most vegetables like cabbage, beets, and carrots grow into enormous size. But the growing season is short and often unpredictable with frequent droughts and summer frosts. Snowfall is heavy but not quite as high as in its closely related alpine counterpart.

Podzol soils everywhere are acid. The rain water leaches out much of the calcium in these soils leaving the subsoils sandy and ashy gray. But the subsoils occur far down beneath the rich black podzols. So old are most of these northern soils that prehistoric wooly mammoths and other large mammals have been recovered from them virtually intact. Generally in the Hudsonian, however, there is not much permanently frozen ground or permafrost, except in the taiga country. Permafrost is characteristic of the tundra lands further north, which are much colder, treeless, and drier.

The great Hudsonian is dominated by the conifers, the spruces, firs, the larch or tamarack, white-cedar, and several pines. As one travels through the length and breadth of this extensive evergreen forest system he cannot help but be struck by the beauty of four very picturesque trees, the red spruce, black spruce, white spruce, and the heavily scented balsam fir.

Red spruce (*Picea rubens,* Sarg.) is the most common spruce of the Adirondack, Green and White Mountains, which make up a major portion of its distribution. It occurs in the St. Lawrence Valley, east through Maine, New Brunswick and Nova Scotia, and is found in pockets of varying size along the Appalachian Mountains south as far as North Carolina. In the south it is limited to slopes and mountain tops above 3,500 feet. It will grow under a forest canopy, but development is slow. It is a medium size tree at maturity, reaching 12 to 24 inches in diameter and 60 to 75 feet in height. The largest trees are usually found in the moisture-laden Appalachian Mountains where growth conditions are more favorable. Soils of the podzolic groups are generally associated with the red spruce range.

Black spruce (*Picea mariana,* Mill.) is one of the most abundant conifers of northern North America. Its range extends from Newfoundland across Canada to Alaska, north to the limit of trees and south to the northern Lake States, northern New York and New England. It will grow on both organic and mineral soils. In the southern part of its range it is associated with peat bogs, muskegs, much-filled seepages and stream courses. To the north it is found on clayey glacial tills and mineral soils. Black spruce commonly occurs as a pure type. In the north it also grows on loams, sandy loams, sands and gravelly or rocky soils, but here it is usually mixed with other species.

Drainage conditions and bog formation are the most significant factors in determining the abundance of black spruce. Over most of its range its two main competitors are tamarack and northern white cedar. As a competitor black spruce has the advantages of being shade tolerant, able to reproduce to a limited extent by "layering" and with persistent and semi-serotinous cones it is able to regenerate quickly on burned-over areas.

While considered to be a small to medium sized tree, the lovely spire-shaped black spruce does grow to a size of 18 inches in diameter and 90 feet in height, on the best sites. On bogs, however, and along the taiga, trees of this species 6 feet high can be well over 100 years old. One small stunted windblown tree in the Churchill, Manitoba, area, while only two inches in diameter, had no fewer than 65 annual rings.

The white spruce (*Picea glauca,* Moench) is considered to be one of the hardiest conifers. It is also a prettier tree than the black, although all spruces, in my judgment, are handsome. Its distribution, with few exceptions, is the same as that of black spruce. It attains greater height and diameter and makes more rapid growth than either red or black spruce and is favored in pulpwood reforestation programs.

White spruce is found from sea level cliffs to mountain areas up to 5,000 feet elevation. Resistance to salt water damage accounts for its presence along wind-swept northern coastlines. White spruce is a tolerant species and will grow on soils varying from heavy clays to alluvial plains. In the New England States the tree is a pioneer species often found invading abandoned fields, while in other parts of its range it is considered a climax species.

Black spruce can be easily distinguished from white spruce by its much shorter needles, which are .3 to .5 of an inch long; while those of white spruce are one inch long and generally crowded on the upper side of the twigs. Their cones also differ markedly in size with those of black spruce .5 to one inch long; while those of white spruce go from 1 to 2.5 inches in length.

The balsam fir *(Abies balsamea)* is the queen conifer of the Hudsonian. Soft and fragrant, it is the Christmas tree from the North. Its range is somewhat similar to black and white spruce except that its northwestern limits stop with western Alberta and eastern British Columbia.

The tamarack *(Larix laricina)* is a deciduous conifer with a range almost as extensive as the black and white spruces. A western species occurs in Idaho, Montana and Washington.

Accompanying the spruces and firs in eastern and central Hudsonian is the northern white-cedar. This tree with its scale-like leaves or needles is a favorite of the bogs and muskegs where deer and moose browse on it extensively. Several different western species occur in more isolated patches in the Rockies, Sierras and Pacific Coast Range.

How did the Hudsonian forest come about? One partial explanation seems plausible. When the earth's continents began to cool, the tropical forests began to shrink from the temperate regions to become concentrated near the equator. When the Rocky Mountains pushed upward they created a vast arid region in the center of the continent where once were found subtropical and tropical seas and steaming swamps and sprawling forests. As the temperate Canadian forests moved southward behind the retreating tropical forest because of changes in climate, it advanced upon the arid mid-continent, divided and spread along the moist mountains on either side. One branch created the eastern deciduous forest we know today, the other fanned over the Rockies to the west coast. As the Sierra Nevadas and Cascade ranges arose, some uplifting for the second time, their mountain chains again created further desert regions on their eastern sides and in the valleys, leaving only temperate forests on their western slopes. So today there are no marked latitudinal zones of vegetation in the United States as marked by temperature changes from north to south. Rather there is, in a complicated fashion, a series of vertical plant kingdoms due to rainfall differences in the north-south mountain ranges. Thus, the two American coasts are forested and the central continent is desert, short grass and prairie.

So the great evergreen forests of Canada and Alaska, as well as those of coastal Oregon, Washington and California, are largely remains of one-time unusual old coniferous forests. But there are oaks and maples and alders in this wilderness, and in California an oak chaparral forest to remind us of this region's one-time connection with the eastern forests when the continents were more level.

The redwood forests of early tropical America have all but disappeared from the eastern part of America, where they once flourished as far as New Jersey. Today these forests are found in remnant form in coastal California and southern Oregon, home of the coast redwood, *Sequoia sempervirens,* and its related *Sequoiadendron giganteum,* the big tree now confined to strictly unglaciated western slopes of the Sierra Nevadas in California.

The giant redwoods we see today are not the same trees that once grew in early times. The early redwoods were the *Metasequoia* or the "dawn redwood." Fossils of this once extensive redwood have been found in Alaska and Oregon. Yet the species still persist in certain valleys in China today, where it grows interspersed with oak, beech, birch and walnut, a true remnant of the flourishing arctic-temperate forests of millions of years ago. When one examines the Chinese redwood and compares it to the fossil redwood of Alaska or Oregon, it is clear that there has been no change in these remarkable trees over the millions of years.

Today's two redwoods in California have great differences in leaf characteristic, the coast redwood looking more like those of the Douglas-fir, while the leaves of the Sierra redwood look more like those of the white-cedar. This is only one of the reasons these two redwoods were recently classified in separate genera. *Sequoiadendron giganteum* used to be known as *Sequoia gigantea.*

For a person who has never seen a redwood, especially one of the huge Sierra redwoods, it is difficult to comprehend their size. So stupendous are these trees that height and girth in trees almost loses its meaning.

In the Calaveras State Park, some eighty miles east of Sacramento, the visitor is introduced to the Big Stump. It belonged to the largest redwood in the Calaveras north grove when the gold rush hit California. The story goes that a man by the name of Dowd first saw this tree and other large sequoias and reported them to his gold prospecting friends on Sutter's Creek. No one believed him. Then one day Dowd emerged from the woods, battered and torn and bleeding, saying he was in a fight with a grizzly and killed it and needed help to drag the bear out. This time some of his friends believed him and went with him to fetch the bear. There was no bear. But Dowd pointed to the giant tree. "There's the giant grizzly," he announced, "what did I tell you." Word about the big tree spread like wildfire. Prospectors came to see it and the grove in their free time. Other people came. Then one group of culprits wondered if it wouldn't be fun to cut the biggest tree down. Can we do it? They tried. For days they worked with axes and saws. But the going was too slow and another method would have to be tried. One man hit on the idea of drilling long holes into the tree—enough holes all the way around to cause it to weaken and fall. Hundreds of holes were drilled but the tree never budged. Then they attacked the tree with more axes and saws and made a huge saw cut almost to the center. They fashioned a huge log battering ram and slammed wedge after wedge into old grizzly. Nothing happened. Seventeen days more of work and the tree still stood. They gave up. Then one night a group of night hunters were camping out near the grove and a big storm came up. A great crash came, the whole forest shook like an earthquake. By lantern light they searched the grove. Sure enough, old grizzly was down at last!

Today, more than a hundred years later, the stump of old grizzly is still plainly visible. So is the main butt of the prostrate giant, the old saw markings, the holes and wedge marks. At eight feet above ground the stump has been sawed off smooth and more than 2,000 annual rings can be counted. Large groups have danced on it, at one time it bore a house and a store. Forty people can stand on it comfortably. How wide was Old Grizzly? I paced it off once and the stump measured 24.1 feet across!

It is indeed gratifying to know that there is much of the great coniferous forest to see today, including preserved groves of some of the remnant giant trees that date far back into the distant past. But more of the big evergreen wilderness must be saved, for once gone, all that it is and all that it was and represents will be no more.

The Hudsonian is the home of a number of wilderness-loving creatures: the marten and the fisher, the wolf and the wolverine; it is also the range of deer, bear, moose, and the woodland caribou. Once incredibly challenging, it is nevertheless a region now fast softening under the heels of human encroachment. Yet the wilderness still possesses much wildness. There are places in the central and northern reaches of this magnificent forest system where human feet have never trod.

No so long ago I ventured into one of these awesome places in the hope of seeing a big bull moose. While this was not in absolute wild country, for me and several companions, it seemed wild enough. I saw no moose, but I came out well recompensed. For a whole week I followed moose tracks in the snow, some larger than those of a giant ox, but never once did fortune smile and allow me to come eyeball to eyeball with a representative of the largest member of the deer family.

I was hunting in the Spanish Lakes country of north-central Ontario, somewhere south of James Bay, and, save for the Arctic tundra, never had a wilderness hold me in such a spell. One day especially, while stalking alone, I put into indelible memory a bone chilling affair. I had followed the tracks of a large moose all morning, going deeper and deeper into the bush, hoping against hope to suddenly spot my antlered giant in some wild muskeg. The noon hour arrived and no moose showed. I commenced to get a little apprehensive for now I was a good eight or nine miles from camp. I began to wonder if I should give up and head back. But the lure of the wilderness is strong and urges one on.

One and two o'clock came and passed and still no prized bull moose appeared. When the sun began to drop I knew it was time to halt. I paused, reflecting, and a thousand thoughts went through my mind. I squinted at the setting sun once more and then sat down on a fallen moss-covered spruce log.

The day was cold but not unpleasant. As the hazy sun filtered its rays down through the balsam trees, so silent and tall and heavily-scented, I felt strangely good inside. The wilderness was cloaked in a deep stillness, a kind of distinct quietness which, surely, reawakens the senses dulled by the din of modern urban places. It is that kind of special peace where pleasant memories return and where fond thoughts are born. Lighting my pipe and puffing leisurely away, I begin thinking how every man and woman in America had the right to experience this kind of pure solitude. Then I thought of how little of this once great boreal forest still remained. Then the spell was broken by two woodsy sounds. It was the chatter of a red squirrel in a distant spruce and the *dee dee* of a black-capped chickadee in some nearby birches. The bird flitted about, came closer, and then perched on a balsam branch overhead. *Chic-chic-a-dee-dee* he said, perhaps as if to ask: "What may you be doing way up here?" With a quiet warmness I responded. "Hello—How nice to see you. I'm really only a guest of your woods. May we be friends?"

When the chickadee finally satisfied its curiosity and flew into the timber, calling out its nostalgic note as these delightful birds do, I arose and looked over my back trail. I had come easily eight miles and it was time to be starting back. As I began to walk, a loon sounded its lonesome cry in the distance and I stopped to listen. The loon kept up its periodic weird laughter and, each time it called, I stopped to hear it.

After several miles of hiking, the first of the Spanish Lakes came into view. Twilight was just beginning to descend. Now for the first time I began sensing the real mood of the great wilderness. Then out of the cold, snow-splashed valley far ahead my ears caught the voice of a lone wild creature. It was a thrilling, awesome sound and it sent massive shivers down my back.

I froze solidly in my tracks and listened . . . breathless. In about a minute it came again, a lonesome *ah . . ooo . . . ooo, ooo . . . ooo, uh, uh, uh, yip, yip,* like a wailing dog caught in the vise of some steel trap. The call came from heavy timber and sounded about a half mile away. Then a second voice joined the first, then a third, and a fourth. With quickening footsteps I plodded ahead, eyes now wide open, scanning all corners of the darkening trail.

When I reached a familiar beaver dam where a small stream audibly gurgled out of the lake, I paused, briefly, to savour the full impact of the strange evening. The area was the last of the semi-open country for from here on into camp the forest got thick and the trail narrowed down to a faint ribbon in the woods. I took in a deep breath and listened.

Once again the stillness was broken by the sounds of the wild. Now one, now two, then a small medley of howling voices. Soon from several directions a whole series of teeth-chattering calls filled the night, voices and howls and barks emanating from a great semi-circle around the lake. It would be mild to say I was uneasy. Even though I was aware that timber wolves were never known to attack humans unless desperate or mad, the thought gave me little comfort. I tightened the grip on my 30-06, tilted back my cap, and with bold new courage took to the trail once more.

The wild serenade continued for some time. And as best as I could calculate there were 14 wolves in that song fest around the lake and, while I knew they were some distance away, the loudness of their howls coupled with the stillness of the night made them appear uncomfortably close.

The wolf pack never closed in around me. Apparently the animals preferred to go on hunting alone, or in twos or threes, and the objects of their chase were snowshoe hares.

When I reached the cabin, hours later, the wolves were still hunting. After dinner I went out on the cabin porch to see if I could hear them again. But one by one the howls grew fainter, less frequent, and farther apart. Apparently the wolf revelry for one night at least was over.

During the night it snowed and by morning the spruce country was covered by six inches of fluffy whiteness. I was up soon after sunup and went outside to a nearby spring. Not a hundred feet from the cabin I came upon the fresh imprints of a wolf, possibly one of the performers of the night before, and was amazed by their size. The tracks were colossal. Breaking two sticks from an alder bush I measured the exact width and length of the largest track. By later check it came to $4\frac{1}{2} \times 6$ inches! A wolf this size, I figured, could easily go to 150 pounds, perhaps even close to 200, surely presenting the figure of a very imposing animal.

The next day I was thrilled to see one of the creatures as he stole swiftly across an open glade not 150 yards ahead of me. He looked taller than any big Russian wolfhound I had ever seen, and were I to measure his height, three feet at the shoulder would not have been an exaggeration. I shall always remember the grace and wildness of this great carnivore as he revealed his presence to me in that flash of less than three seconds.

The wolf is a noble creature. No one knows for sure how many still inhabit the North American continent. Extirpated from most of the continental United States, the gray wolf or timber wolf continues to hold his own in the great spruce-fir wilderness of Canada and Alaska. However, recent authoritative sources have put the wolf population in Canada at only 30,000 and most of these are found in the Hudsonian wilderness.

Wolf stories are intriguing. Jack London's remarkable saga of how a great, semi-wild wolf periodically answered the call of the wild is one of the best. One episode in particular is a thriller. This is the one where the lone dog-wolf took after a giant moose and pursued it relentlessly day after day, finally pulling the big bull down. While such an occurrence is plausible with an old moose, most biologists I've talked to about wolf-moose relationships disclaim any such stories. Durward Allen, a wildlife biologist of considerable note and a scientist who has observed wolves and moose on Michigan's Isle Royale, says that a wolf is no match for an adult moose. A strong moose can ward off any timber wolf, even a whole pack. A healthy moose, Dr. Allen says, is full of fight and will discourage a wolf or wolves in a few seconds or minutes. He may do this by simply standing and defying them, or he may merely trot away through the deep snow and tangled blowdowns where the shorter-legged wolf soons wears out and quits. A weak and unhealthy moose, especially an old animal, will try to run away and usually is injured in the hams and made to stand. In such instances the wolves may pile in and grab on anywhere or they may sit about and wait for their victim to stiffen up. Sometimes an injured moose actually is finished off by a loner after the pack has left it and moved on, only to come back later and feast. A single wolf, however, is not likely to knock a moose over. The popular notion that wolves hamstring their victims is fictional.

Moose today are still plentiful in much of the great Hudsonian-Canadian muskeg country of Canada and Alaska. The muskeg is a sort of transition zone between the dense spruce-fir-cedar forests and open bog. These low areas are rich in mosses, lichens, grasses and sedges. In many places the muskegs contain small dark pools of water with lily pads and other floating vegetation growing thickly in them. To these places the moose come by day, sometimes alone, often in small family groups—a bull, cow and calf or yearling—to feed, romp or just spend the hours. After they have fed they amble back into the coniferous forests where there is more protection.

In the winter, which is most of the time in moose country, moose, like deer, are browsing animals, feeding on young woody growth of the cutovers and frequenting other areas of early forest succession.

One July day I flew a transect over typical moose country in Alaska and counted 55 moose—adults and young—in one hour. I was flying with Jim King of the United States Fish and Wildlife Service, a splendid pilot and naturalist, and who knows Alaska moose like a rancher knows his cattle. We took off from an airfield near Fairbanks and headed for the muskeg country. The technique was to fly a straight transect for ten miles, then turn right a mile and take another parallel transect back. Back and forth we flew over a wide range of timber and muskegs, spotting moose in almost every large opening. When we noted an unusually large bull with a cow and young, Jim nudged me and we went down for a good look, dropping to 800 feet, 600 feet, and then finally leveling off at about 500. As we swooped over the feeding monarch, he threw up his rocking-chair-like antlers and gave us a good challenging shake of the head. Sometimes a whole group would be startled and take off a short distance. In most cases, however, the moose took our intrusion in stride, and when we passed on they returned to their quiet business of feeding and munching on browse plants or simply basking in the sunlight in their soggy domain.

But moose and wolves are not the only significant inhabitants of the Hudsonian wilderness. There are three other mammals in particular which find the Canadian-Hudsonian forest to their liking: marten, fisher, and wolverine. All are members of the weasel family, although the wolverine looks more like a cross between a badger and a bear than a weasel. All are typically weasel in habit, wild, usually vicious, and entirely carnivorous, feeding largely upon rodents and other animals.

The marten is the most beautiful of the three—in fact, the handsomest member of the entire weasel family. In years past it was abundant in nearly all northern coniferous forests. One year Canada exported to France over 30,000 skins of the marten. Today the fleet-footed, big-eyed, restless animal of the spruce-fir timber is down in its numbers. Lumbering, overtrapping, forest fires and general human encroachment are mainly responsible for its depletion. In addition, habitat destruction, particularly the cutting out of large, virgin timber stands, has been a factor. Marten prefer big trees and seek out dens in the oldest, most overmature spruce forests. The marten and the ways of man are not compatible. Everywhere man's encroachment on the wilderness has played havoc with the marten.

A quality one must admire in the marten is curiosity. Almost any odd object will attract this creature—a red feather, piece of yellow rag, an angler's lost bucktail fly in the tree tops, even an empty sardine can. One reason the marten is easy to trap and, perhaps, why its population has become so drastically reduced is this quality of inquisitiveness. A marten is about the size of a long, slinking alley cat, with males averaging between 5 and 7 pounds, females a little smaller. The average total length of a marten, including about a 10-inch tail, is 24 inches.

The fisher is a close but larger cousin of the marten and is frequently referred to as the big marten. A good sized male will average 12 pounds and range in length from 30 to 40 inches. So agile and fleet-footed is this prized furbearer that it can overtake and kill a marten. When it comes down a tree headfirst and meets a human intruder,

Dropping to a low position, I crept closer for a better view, finally reaching a small fir tree. Using the evergreen as a brace and screen, I raised myself over the precipice.

The wolf, a big gray male with fangs bared, was circling his tormentor, body arched sideways and snarling viciously. His adversary hugged the ground, slamming the gravel trail first with one front foot, then another, teeth snapping audibly like a vicious dog and emitting a series of terrifying growls. There had been no body contact that I could see, but then it came, the wolverine swiftly leaping and throwing his full weight against the wolf. But the wolf tore him loose with a double lightning shake of his head, tearing out enormous chunks of fur from his attacker. The smash was a glancing blow and the wolf took it well, his grappler once more on the ground. Again, they circled. Gulo feinted a spring, then rolled partly over, head low, gripping the ground for another attack. He was aiming for a throat siege this time but the wolf backed away. Then an unfortunate thing happened. A loose rock from my overlook spoiled it all. A small stone and some loose bits of gravel went spilling down the bank and onto the trail below and the combatants sensing alarm, separated quickly and bounded away in opposite directions. What might have been a much more lasting fight ended in a draw, adding another thrilling page of mystery to the Canadian coniferous wilderness—a saga of life in the wild the real outcome of which no human being will ever know.

The encounter taught me a profound lesson, that man can find in the living great wilderness the essence of all wildness, a quality which brings out nature's basic wisdom in relationship to man's. Out of this wildness, out of the wild wolverine, as well as the antelope, peccary, gila woodpecker, the sea otter and grunion, honey bee and the crab, man can learn the tenets of coexistence and survival. If the wilderness teaches us anything, it teaches us—those willing to be taught—that in the wild world lies much of the destiny of man.

THE ARCTIC TUNDRA

HIGH UPON THE FOREHEAD OF OUR TWIRLING GLOBE, BEYOND THE LONG line of nature realms from the equatorial forest to the dwindling taiga, lies the final land of a finite world—the Arctic kingdom. Remote and incredibly big, it is the country that lies beyond everything else— beyond all roads, beyond the last of the coniferous trees, the land called "beyond the north wind."

Just as the tropical wilderness is a marvelous environment, so too is the Arctic world, a biome of unfamiliar and often fantastic scenes and of little known but extraordinary happenings. Still largely wild and isolated and far removed from most human eyes, it is a land that throbs with a spellish influence over all that dwells there permanently or comes to see it seasonally.

To know this strange world, one should first of all know something of its geography, its physical elements, its strange beauty and stark reality and, most important, its fascinating life. And to know all these in their fullest measure one should, I suspect, visit the Arctic tundra at least once and see and feel this awe-inspiring land for himself.

The tundra world alone is a three-part world. It begins where the taiga ends. At this point the zone of demarcation is unmistakable. It is a kind of no-man's-land that defies classification. South of this line one

begins to see scrawny coniferous trees and these in a hundred or several hundred miles graduate and group into forests. North of the demarcation line the landscape opens treeless and wide and wanting, and then flows onward in a seemingly never-ending plain. These are the so-called "Arctic barrens," which, surprisingly, are not barren at all. They are the extensive dry-weather plains of the Arctic and in North America number seven million square miles of cold country. But the tundra world has two additional faces, the countenance of rugged mountains and headlands, sometimes referred to as the high Arctic, and the low country of northern islands known as the "Low Arctic of the Archipelago." These combined worlds of the Arctic, not counting Greenland, which is part of North America, make up another one million square miles.

The Arctic tundra is a desolate, remorseless land, where everything spells struggle and all that's visible and much that is invisible bears the telltale marks of a hostile environment. But the land and the waters are not completely hostile, for life forms abound in unbelievable style and number.

And the Arctic and the Arctic tundra are not completely one entity. The former is a vast geographic region, the latter, a somewhat smaller area but still a major land ecosystem.

Most people consider the Arctic and the tundra a completely frigid and desolate environment, a region of perpetual ice and snow, a world of horrible blizzards and incredibly low temperatures. While at times the Arctic region does display these characteristics, the truth is that the Arctic is far different than what popular notion has led us to believe. The erroneous impression is understandable since much of the image we get of the Arctic has come from the exploits of polar explorers who have spent adventurous weeks, months, even years, on and around the ice pack in an effort to reach the North Pole.

But the ice pack, which is in reality a frozen sea over the Arctic Ocean basin, is not the Arctic alone. Geographically speaking, the Arctic includes a vast expanse of country above 66 degrees, 30 minutes north latitude to the North Pole. The latitude demarcation is purely mathematical and is used primarily for navigation and astronomical study. Ecologically, however, the Arctic embraces all the lands and waters above the treeline—that is, an uneven line north and south of the Arctic Circle above which no tree life appears. It includes the great Arctic barrens, the icy mountains, and the islands of the Arctic Archipelago. The true Arctic, then, is a vast part of our earth's surface, covering millions of square miles, an area roughly three times the size of the continental United States. It is a circumpolar region, touching Alaska, Canada, Greenland, Norway, Sweden, Finland and Russia.

The Arctic around the North Pole is water, not land, and for the most part is perpetually frozen to make up the Arctic ice pack. Beneath this sprawling, ever-changing ice mass, is the central Arctic Sea marked by a deep basin with a high subterranean ridge. The continental shelves around the Arctic seas project northward like vast rims. In fact, these undersea rims are the longest in the world, especially in Russia, where in some places they extend outward as much as 800 miles. The central basin of the Arctic Ocean, roughly 700 by 1,400 miles in size, goes to 6,000 feet in depth. Some sea chasms, however, reach down as much as 15,000 feet. In contrast, Hudson Bay, which is a shallow sea, averages only 650 feet in depth.

There is also much misunderstanding about Arctic temperatures and weather.

It gets cold in the Arctic but colder temperatures have been recorded in sub-Arctic Siberia, and in Montana, Minnesota, even in one frost pocket in northern New York. Over the entire Arctic coast there is no record of temperatures going below −55 degrees F. With the exception of Greenland, which is a land plateau with bordering mountains and a huge basin filled with ice, nine-tenths of all Arctic lands are free of ice and snow in the summer.

And although winter temperatures in the inland Arctic have been recorded as low as 90 degrees below zero, and this in Siberia, summer temperatures may rise as high as 70 degrees, even higher. One July day at Fort Yukon, Alaska, I saw the temperature go into the eighties. This same area once experienced a temperature of over 100 degrees. Summer temperatures in some parts of Alaska would be called hot in Tennessee or South Carolina. Much of this is due to the warming waters of the West Wind Drift which brings warm central Pacific waters to the western coast of Alaska. Another warming current in the east, the North Atlantic Drift, brings mild weather to Iceland and the northern coasts of Scandinavia. Summer rains, rather than snows, have occurred even at the North Pole. The average winter temperature for the Arctic region is an unbelievable 30 degrees F. And along much of the Arctic coast, the winds in the summer time usually blow from the sea, while in the winter they blow from the land.

And, contrary to general belief, too, there are extensive forests in parts of the southern Arctic. In a region marked by a mixture of stunted evergreen trees and open tundra, there are often extensive stands of spruce, fir, birch, alder, and willow. In Alaska and the northwestern sub-Arctic Canada, the dominant tree species is white spruce; in Labrador and Quebec it is black spruce, with a good representation of tamarack or larch. When trees give out to the vast stretches of tundra with their low, soggy blankets of dwarf plants, mostly Arctic grasses, lichens and mosses, the predominant cause is dry winds rather than cold. About 1,700 different kinds of plants have been identified in the Arctic, including 900 different wildflowers.

While the tundra world is a land of long cold winters and much darkness, its brief summers have perpetual sunlight. This results in speedy growth and much living activity. And while life forms are not great, numbers can be very large.

The tundra is the home of the lichen, lemmings, and Lapland longspur, of seal and walrus and the slant-eyed, brown-skinned men once from another land who hunt them. It is the treeless territory of the wandering Arctic grizzly and the ever-searching great ice bear (polar bear) and a smallish Arctic marmot the natives call *sik sik*. It is the hunting ground of the great white wolf and birds that hover and swoop and scold when a strange visitor emerges on the scene.

The tundra is strutting legs and scurrying feet over a desolate landscape: rock and willow ptarmigan blending with the rocks, small

years ago, that left much of the Arctic in the condition in which we see it today. When the latest polar ice cap retreated, life, including certain plants and animals, and man, moved in.

The Arctic tundra forms a treeless carpet of permafrost ground and numerous lakes and potholes around the Arctic Ocean and southward to Iceland, Laborador, Hudson Bay, the Mackenzie Delta, and the Brooks Range, in Alaska. In the North Pacific, it skirts the Bering Sea and extends across Siberia and from the Bering Straits to the Aleutians. There is almost no counterpart to the Arctic tundra in the Southern Hemisphere, as the continent of Antarctica is largely covered by ice. There are, however, isolated areas of tundra-like conditions on some of the sub-Antarctic islands south of New Zealand in the Indian Ocean and on South Georgia in the South Atlantic; also some tundra-like conditions prevail on most high mountaintops around the globe, even in equatorial Africa, although the bulk of the high meadows one sees in these areas are more properly "alpine tundras." The true tundras and alpine tundras differ in that the former is characterized by much permafrost which alpine meadows do not have to any great extent, plus the fact that true tundras have long periods of daylight in the summer which their alpine counterparts do not have. Altitudinal differences also exist which have given rise to possibly different generic races of plants which have learned to live under varying conditions of light and altitude. Both tundras, however, are cold and fragile environments and largely dominated by the grasses, sedges, and prostrate-growing dwarf willows.

Plant productivity is low in Arctic plants. Based upon the entire year, the above-ground productivity of Arctic vegetation is usually less than a gram of dry matter (biomass) produced per square meter per day; based upon the growing season it may range from one to four grams per square meter per day. This is not much growth compared to other major ecosystems, yet it is sufficient to withstand the life that is present. This is because the grasseaters are very few in species, although they can be large in colonial groups with migrating habits. Because the tundra is so vast, the transient herbivores, like the caribou, are able to gather enough food as they wander from place to place. But any continuous cropping of tundra vegetation portends danger, for the plants recover very slowly, some indeed never recover. So the cold, shallow-soiled tundras are terribly fragile places where man's impact, if not guarded, can be very marked indeed. A snowmobile track over the tundra plains may remain visible for ten years; an Arctic lake with its fish thrown off balance by overfishing may not recover for a hundred years.

Arctic vegetation is also heavily rooted, that is, much of the plant productivity goes into the production of root systems—regular spreading roots, rhizomes and tubers. Such migrating or emigrating mammals as caribou, musk ox, lemmings and hares move about and find the tops of plants their prime food source. The smaller plant-eaters, or herbivores, stay put more and feed on bulbs, rhizomes, and other root parts.

The Arctic tundra also exhibits vegetational productivity and animal populations in cyclic fashion. In good years with high vegetational yields, there is a tendency for the number of rodents, mostly lemmings and hares, to be high. This seems to cause a high buildup among the flesh-eaters, or carnivores, such as ermine, foxes, owls, and wolves. When plant yield is low, a corresponding "crash" may occur among the rodents, followed by a drop in the population of carnivores. Birds, like the snowy owl, may fly further southward in the winter in search of needed food.

In good years when the short-lived summers have sufficient rain, the Arctic tundra, in brief periods, can become a colorful floristic world of many Lilliputian blooming plants. This usually occurs in late June, July, and early August. When this happens, the whole greenish-purplish tundra is suddenly transformed into a great unending magical carpet.

One morning following a night of light rain on the Canadian central "barrens" I was treated to one of these beautiful floral displays. So dramatic was the change in the vegetation that I could not believe my eyes. I was with a Canadian biologist, Robert A. Ruttan, and a small group of Eskimos, south of Bathurst Inlet and with a group of them, we went out exploring our new-found Lilliputian Garden of Eden. Most abundant everywhere were the white composite flowers of Labrador tea. Then came the purple saxifrage, in clump after clump, and tiny dwarf pink rhododendron. In the lowlands grew sprays of Arctic cottongrass and tiny Arctic iris. There were small buttercups and yellow Arctic avens on the hillsides. Over the fresh green landscape grew many stems of grass-of-parnassus and miniature bluebells. Most of the wildflowers were white, but lots were pink, red, purple, lavender, and gold. Some of the very tiniest flowers I had ever seen, barely visible through a magnifying lens, were mere specks of crimson or yellow. My Eskimo friends and I began gathering samples of different wildflowers and by noon we had collected 87 different species or varieties of species, including hatfuls of delicious boleti (fungi) for dinner. Botanists are not in agreement as to the total number of identified plants in the North American Arctic. The figures range from 800 to 1,500, depending upon the authority one uses, but decidedly there are far more plants present than were once believed to be there. And while the number may be somewhat less than in alpine biomes, their total, nonetheless, is impressive. Admittedly, several thousand species of plants which seem a reasonable estimate of the total number now identified in the Arctic, may seem low compared to the equatorial tropics where the number runs to hundreds of thousands, but the Arctic plant world, nevertheless, is substantial.

In the days that followed I learned much about Arctic plants from the Eskimos and also how these people are able to survive in the Northland. Later, with additional research, I was able to piece together the wonderful saga of these people.

The history of the Eskimo in North America is a fascinating story. Ethnologists, anthropologists and archeologists agree these people are a remarkable ethnic group. Some experts on Eskimo culture consider these people the most unique, if not the most remarkable, of aborigines in the New World. Apparently the belief these days is universal that these people came out of central Asia. The accepted view is that they emigrated across some 6,000 miles of the Arctic coastland from Cape Siberia and then spread all the way to eastern Greenland. These people, furthermore, are surprisingly uniform in many ways—in physical characteristics, habits, and language. Nowhere else on the globe has an ethnic group spread itself so widely over northern lands as has the Eskimo.

For some time many ethnologists have believed that these people were late comers to the New World. Now there is sufficient archeological proof to show that this is not so. Recent discoveries tend to prove that the Eskimo was well established in his western sector at the time of Christ and even some years before. Remains of pottery, stone implements, and artifacts tested with Carbon 14 show that these people were the real Eskimo ancients. They exhibited a very distinct culture a long time ago. There is belief too that even earlier remains of their existence may be found.

But the Eskimo's origin in north central Asia is shrouded in archeological obscurity. In Arctic Siberia the several languages and culture groups there are not like the more uniform culture of Arctic America. Their development resulted, apparently, from several separate movements northward. Some groups followed larger river courses to the Arctic coast. Artifacts from the Or River and Lake Baikal are said to resemble those of the ancient Eskimo. One of these great emigrations out of central Asia occurred around 200 to 50 B.C. This group halted for a while at the Bering Sea, across from present-day Alaska, because of an unusual abundance of nature's riches—walrus, seal, and the beluga white whale. There were also fish and birds which gave the people a great sufficiency of everything and they thrived.

As the population grew and the hardy men became proficient in their skin-covered umiaks, they swarmed over the waters of the Straits, spilling onto the Diomedes and other intermediate islands. Soon many of them established villages and small groups on the Alaskan coast. These were the Old Bering Sea People, small in stature but hardy, strong, and as courageous as any humans on earth. They stalked seals and huge bull walrus. Not infrequently, they attacked the king of Arctic beasts, the polar bear. When black and white killer whales schooled in the ice waters, throngs of fearless men and courageous older boys took their umiaks and put into the choppy waters and attacked the killers. The savage whales fought back tearing at the small boats but the sharp harpoons finally proved too much and the waters turned red. Soon enormous white-black bellies floated to the surface. Then the work of recovering and carving up the huge creatures would begin.

Some of these ancient maritime dwellers paid for their feats with their lives—but the spirit that dwelt within them survived and strengthened. Ethnologists say that these Bering Sea people are the first Eskimos of which we have definite knowledge, yet there is general belief that a still earlier group came from coastal, northeastern Asia and spread into Arctic America.

The aboriginal Eskimos made fire by taking two iron pyrites and striking them together to send sparks into tinder. The tinder could be most anything from musk ox wool, dried Arctic cotton grass balls, or even human hair. The larger the rocks, the greater was the spark and the easier to get the fire started. Once a fire got going in a village or camp, it almost never was allowed to go out. Someone always would have a fire from which others could be ignited. Most fires were kept aflame in stone lamps into which was inserted a wick of dry moss. The lamps not only provided some heat for the snowhouses but also interior light during the long, dark winters.

From the Alaskan northwest the Bering Sea Eskimos pushed outward. One group moved along the coast north-eastward, another southward. Then about a thousand years later a sudden expansion occurred, perhaps motivated by new tools and ideas coming over from Asia. New and better inventions of iron and slate and bone brought good times and the population soared. The resulting pressures moved the Eskimo still further eastward along the coast and did not stop until it reached Greenland and Newfoundland. So bold and swift was the eastern expansion that the Eskimos encountered no other inhabitants until they reached Hudson Bay.

Today archeologists refer to the Bering Sea Eskimo as Panuk and those in the Eastern Arctic as Thule. Customs have changed considerably and there now is some seasonal migration, especially among those populations of the Central Arctic. In the winter the Eskimo stayed close to the sea ice, living off seal and walrus. During the summer they moved inland in search of caribou, musk ox, small mammals, birds, and fish.

In comparative recent times some of the so-called "caribou" Eskimos stayed on in the Arctic "barrens" all year long, moving only slightly from one hunting and trapping territory to the next. To ease their take of caribou in Canada, the government began to subsidize certain groups with food, clothing and other provisions. They set up schools for them such as the one at Innuvik, 350 miles north of the Arctic Circle, in the Mackenzie Delta.

One day on the "barrens" I asked Amy, our Eskimo cook, how she liked her three years in school at civilized Innuvik. She replied hesitatingly with a high-pitched: "I like it." But the truth is modern life in most northern villages offers little but degradation to the freedom-loving, self-reliant Eskimo. Perhaps Simon, one of our tagging crew Eskimos, put it most clearly when he said that Indian and white man villages "no good . . . we just shovel white man's garbage."

In the true Arctic the Eskimo is still loose, still untied like the north wind. His wants are few, pleasures simple. His burden is arduous but not unpleasant. With traded furs and skins he can now buy tobacco and groceries and such rare luxuries as boats, motors, gasoline, even Skidoos. Yet much of the Eskimos' life even today is primitive, living in tents or shacks in the summer and snowhouses in the winter, traveling along inland and coastal waters in the summer by kayak and umiak, a large boat used mainly to transport family groups. In the winter travel is on foot, dog team, or Skidoo.

Like the Indian tribes in and around the tree country, the Crees and Chipeweyans, the Eskimos keep lots of dogs but unlike their traditional enemies, they treat their canines well. Indians often starve their dogs in the summer, taking back the stragglers and the most hardy when cold weather arrives and their usefulness is once more apparent. Not so the Eskimo. His dogs are well cared for all year through.

I asked Joseph, another Eskimo, why this was so and he grinned. Simon smiled. Amy said nothing. They knew the answer but would not say.

"It's because the Indian has become contaminated with the ugly ways of the white man," Bob Ruttan, my Canadian biologist host, put in. Amy blushed a little and turned to her teapot on the stove. There was a moment of silence. Then she turned around, grinned, and announced, "Tea, she is ready."

The Arctic kingdom is a great place for birds. While the number of species falls short of temperate and tropic climes, still over one hundred forms bring grace and song to this hostile land, including some ninety species in one area. From the standpoint of wildlife, the Arctic is one of the most important regions for the production of waterfowl.

Both the lesser and greater snow goose makes the Arctic its summer home, a species whose very name suggests migration to "the land beyond the north wind." Most of the other geese—the blue goose, cackling goose, emperor goose and the Canada goose—all are breeders on the Arctic tundra. The interior tundra contributes little to the production of ducks. Old squaws and eider ducks occur in low densities but are usually found in the coastal areas.

The tundra lands along the coastline and the coastal plain, both on the mainland and on the Arctic islands, provide the most attractive waterfowl habitat in the Arctic. Great numbers of breeding waterfowl exist there, especially colonial nesters such as the snow goose. Not only do all species of geese nest in one or another of the many coastal tundra situations but, collectively, these areas produce most of the North American geese. Coastal tundras in Alaska and in the western Arctic produce all of the emperor geese, cackling geese, black brant, and most of the white fronted geese. Coastal areas in the Northwest Territories and in the Arctic islands produce the bulk of the American brant, the smaller races of the Canadas, and the blue and snow geese. Even among the large Canadas a significant portion of the population is produced in coastal tundras of the Ungava Peninsula in northern Quebec.

The most relentless factor affecting Arctic birds is time. The brief summer of the Arctic demands that living things waste no time if they are to perpetuate their kind. But the long Arctic days and their many hours of sunlight compensate somewhat for the shortness of the season. All biological processes are incredibly dynamic; here, the rapidity of change in natural events is astounding. When breeding waterfowl arrive in June, they settle down at once to the business in hand. Nesting and brooding cannot be delayed if the young are to be on the wing before freeze up.

Many Arctic birds breed in great colonies and thus compensate partially for the shortage of bird species. But even in the winter the Arctic is never entirely free of some birds. Surprisingly, one may see or hear birds at even the highest latitudes, such as the appearance of the snowy owl or a snow bunting, or occasionally hear the croak of a raven.

The most abundant colonial bird in the Arctic is the thick-billed murre or akpa. These are penguin-like birds and occupy the same niche in the Arctic as do their counterparts, the penguins, in the Antarctic. The murres breed in the millions along the Arctic seaside cliffs and each spring and late summer their comings and goings produce one of the great spectacles in birddom. The birds in the spring carry out strange but beautiful joy-flights and underwater dances which are believed to stimulate breeding. The later summer mass departure of the adults and young, is also a spectacle. At this time the adults congregate at the base of the cliffs and start calling to their young on the cliff. The young hurtle out of the nests and land in the sea unhurt, whereupon the parents take them out to sea. It is three years before the young mature and return to the cliffs to start the parental cycle all over again.

The Arctic is, for the most part, a new region for birds. Because of extensive glaciation, relatively few birds migrate north, although more are going all the time. The Hudson Bay lowlands is especially a new area for birds.

Perhaps the most intriguing aspect of the Arctic is its bird gathering spots. Places like Churchill, on Hudson Bay, the sea islands of the Hudson straits and the eastern Canadian Archipelago, and the Yukon Delta, are favorite gathering areas for nesting birds and thereby constitute an ornithologist's paradise.

Some of the birds in the Far North are used for food by the Eskimos and Indians. Some of the most abundant birds in Arctic lands are waterfowl, ravens, falcons, snowbirds and sandpipers. Ptarmigan are common on the open tundra. Puffins, petrels, and auks nest on the sea islands and lowlands along the coast. Besides murres, dovekies, gulls and sea pigeons nest along the Arctic cliffs.

One small marsh bird, the sora, finds the Arctic tundra its principal nesting home. This awkward rail, appearing very much like a tiny flightless chicken—and in the air appearing like a bunch of rags—flies south in the autumn from the Hudson Bay region all the way to the fresh water marshes of eastern United States.

Several common summer Arctic residents fly southward incredible distances. These birds are not content to stop in northern South America but push on across the Equator on down to the pampas of Argentina.

Of all North American land birds, one group has the longest migration route of all. The birds of this group fly to the Yukon Territory and Alaska, in the summer, then migrate south in the winter to Argentina—7,000 miles away. The seasonal flights of some birds are exceeded in length by the journeys of several species of water birds, principally members of the sub-order of shorebirds. In this group are found 19 species that nest north of the Arctic Circle and winter in South America. Of this group six species migrate as far south as Patagonia. Thus a number of birds have migration routes of 8,000 miles or more.

The champion "globe-trotter" of them all is the Arctic tern. The name "Arctic" is well earned, as the breeding range of this bird is circumpolar, nesting as far north as it can find a suitable place to rear its young. The first nest to be found in the high Arctic was only 7-½ degrees from the North Pole. It contained a downy chick encased by a wall of newly fallen snow that had been scooped out by the parent.

The Arctic tern in North America seems to breed southward in the interior to Great Slave Lake and on the Atlantic coast to Massachusetts. After the young are grown these birds vanish from their North American breeding grounds only to reappear a few months later in the Antarctic—some 11,000 miles away. Until very recently the route followed by these strong fliers was a complete mystery. While a few scattered individuals have been noted south as far as Long Island, the species was otherwise practically unknown along the Atlantic coasts of North and South America. It was, however, known to be a migrant along the west coast of Europe and Africa. By means of numbered bands and many records, the picture is now developing that gives the Arctic tern credit for making the most remarkable and longest of all migratory bird journeys in the world.

Drawn to the Arctic seas are a number of marine mammals, such as seals, walrus, and whales, including the white beluga, the killer whale, and the giant blue whale. The waters must be partially free of ice for these animals which means that they are mostly partially open water migrants. A few species, like certain seals, can remain around and under the ice all winter with the help of blow holes. It is the seal which forms the chief food source for the polar bear. Some 120 kinds of fish are caught in Arctic seas, mostly in sub-Arctic open waters, with halibut, cod and flounder the principal species. Some salmon, grayling, and Arctic char are also taken.

The Arctic stronghold is also the territory of five terrestrial wanderers. One, the great ice bear, or polar, is as much an ice rover as anything else, going only infrequently onto the land. The others are completely land based and wander either in one region or great distances. These are the barrenground grizzly, Arctic wolf, musk ox, and the barrenground caribou.

The barrenground grizzly is confined to the Arctic mainland and is a smaller counterpart of the Alaskan grizzly. While it is largely a feeder on Arctic ground squirrels, it will eat fish, birds, grubs and roots. Unlike its white polar bear cousin which roams the sea ice the year-round, the barrenground grizzly holes up for part of the winter. One Arctic mammal, the *sik sik* or ground squirrel truly hibernates—that is, its body temperature drops to near the freezing point with breathing limited to two or three times per minute.

The polar bear is a hard-pressed animal, pursued relentlessly by the Eskimos and some white hunters. Its numbers have been reduced sharply until today, by international agreement, the annual polar bear take has become limited. Circumpolar in its range, the bear wanders over the ice for hundreds of miles, looking for seal, its principal food.

The other large carnivore to grace the Arctic landscape is the great white wolf or Arctic wolf. It is a large creature with huge feet and is a part of the Arctic environment as is the migrating caribou, upon which it largely feeds. The wolf, however, also feeds on ground squirrels, lemmings, voles, hares, ptarmigan and other birds, and an occasional musk ox. It occupies a vital role in the Arctic ecosystem where it has lived in harmonious relationship with its prey, the herbivores, as well as with its other related warm-blooded creatures. Were it not for the wolf, certainly the musk ox, Arctic hares, and the caribou would not remain in a balanced condition with the food supply.

Of the last two Arctic tundra wanderers, the musk ox and the caribou, it must be said that they are champions in their own right. Both are incredible mammals.

The musk ox is a low statured shaggy beast that braves the Arctic as isolated individual outcasts or groups ranging from five to fifty. Large bulls may reach 1,000 pounds while the cows will go 250 to 300 pounds less. These animals move over the tundra a great deal in search of food but do not migrate like the caribou. If attacked, they would rather go into a defense ring, bulls and cows, with the horned heads outward, and the young inside. Swaying back and forth, shoulder to shoulder, the bone and sinew groups make an impregnable circle. Sometimes a charging grizzly or wolf may be successful in breaking open the defense ring and snatching a calf, but not often.

The musk ox feeds on dwarf willow and birch, sedges and brown moss plants which are rich in protein. In the winter it seeks the snowless, windswept areas, pawing through the ice for scrawny food plants— yet somehow, it survives. About 21,000 musk ox are said to be in Arctic Canada and another 5,000 in Greenland. A few survive on Arctic islands only 420 miles from the North Pole.

The musk ox is really not a wild ox, but a member of a special family, like the goats, its closest relative being the tarkin in Tibet. As a species, it is strictly North American.

The champion land trotter of the Arctic stronghold is the caribou. Several forms occur in the Arctic and sub-Arctic region of North America. The genus *Rangifer* is circumpolar and includes Old World reindeer and New World caribou. The woodland caribou *(Rangifer caribou)* occurs largely in the Hudsonian coniferous forest from Newfoundland to the Rockies. The stone caribou is the most common big game animal in Alaska; perhaps 400,000 now occur in that state. The whitish Peary caribou is not too migratory and is largely confined to Ellesmere Island, other northern Arctic islands, and in northern Greenland as far north as 83 degrees latitude. There is also the Grant caribou found on the Alaskan Peninsula and on Unimak Island. The most abundant of all caribou is the barrenground caribou *(Rangifer arcticus),* a truly amazing rover of the taiga forests and the desolate tundra. Perhaps two to three million of these animals occur on the North American continent.

Most male caribou range in size from 150 to 400 pounds with females from 50 to 100 pounds less. Their height at shoulder level runs from 3½ to 4½ feet. An interesting feature is that in the caribou both sexes have antlers—the only instance of its kind in the North American deer family.

To know the great Arctic wanderer, the barrenground caribou, one should try to follow it across the tundra and in the taiga on a year-around cycle. Calendar-wise, the caribou cycle begins and ends in darkness. The new year unfolds on the tundra with most of the barrenground caribou gone from the cold dark prairies. Those that remain to brave the cold are stragglers, or small groups of the less migratory Peary caribou, found mostly on the islands of the Arctic Archipelago. Both are vulnerable to the hard-pressed wolves. But the main barren-ground caribou herds are safely sheltered in the coniferous taiga far south of treeline.

For weeks following the new year the entire northern tundra is shrouded in a strange kind of semi-twilight. Daylight comes as a grayish glow, remains only a few hours (usually a little before noon and a short period in the afternoon) then gives way to darkness. There are cloudy days when even the short daylight hours are absorbed into a darkness, like the eerie, lightless cast from an eclipse of the sun.

There is deathly silence in this world, a silence broken occasionally by the foot scrapings of musk ox as a small band paws through lowland ice in search of brown moss, or the wail of an Arctic wolf as he peers from some lofty rimrock across a vast expanse of nothingness. Or, in a much smaller world, the faint scurrying rustle of a lemming around a frozen glacial erratic. And, in some far away coastal places, like along the Arctic Sea, there is the awesome rumble of cracking and shifting ice.

But when the winds of March and April come with their corresponding longer days of light and warmth, a restless mood descends upon the Arctic. A golden-eyed owl on silent wings, white as snow, sweeps around the musk ox in search of food. Soon the ptarmigan and the Arctic hare grow restive. More lemmings steal out of their ice-packed burrows with some bolder than others venturing out onto the wet snow. Many never return. The long nights are shorter now and the dawns unfold early.

May arrives and a whole new chain of life begins—the tundra greens up in spots long brown, the snow geese arrive along the tundra fringe, and the musk ox circles wider and wider for moss, and drops its young. Now the restless caribou in the taiga begin to stir. They are lean and hungry from long confinement in the semi-open coniferous forests, for browse in some yards has become very scant. Suddenly they begin to move, small bands at first led by young bulls, then larger groups, then larger bands still, bulls and cows and yearlings. From distant ranges they come, from the birch woods, from aspen and larch thickets; from the great white spruce lands stretching from Hudson Bay on to far-off Alaskan ranges they come. They move in great bands, in some districts numbering into the thousands, moving, steadily moving, northward. More young and old bulls appear and more pregnant and dry cows. More yearlings come. The line is long and dozens of the oldest cows and bulls, as well as the sick and the feeble, lag behind. These are prime targets for the wolves and, on occasions, a solitary wolverine or an Arctic barrenground grizzly.

By late May and early June the roaming bands of twitching caribou gather into stupendous herds and one morning, the mass of animaldom breaks out full force onto the tundra plains, great bunches moving, halting, now feeding, now resting. Occasionally strong single bulls or groups of cows fight off the wolves. On they go, on to the great north country cold prairies, on for 500 and 1,000 miles, where new life awaits and summer begins. The herd splits up and the bulls go one way, cows another. Calves are born. Some of the very young are sick or too weak and die, only to be devoured by foxes, wolves, gyrfalcons and owls. Light rains come and wildflowers appear, delicate bluebells, saxifrage, dwarf rhododendron, Arctic avens. The wild geese have come, paired off, and made their nests. Soon they will reveal their young and the parents will molt. Along the Arctic icy shore, the polar bear hunts seal and young walrus. His coat is yellowish-white now from good hunting and much meat.

When late August comes and frosty nights descend even as early as in the afternoon, a few caribou bulls sniff the northwind, turn around, and begin heading south. Soon they are joined by the cows and the young.

Now the long trek across the tundra to the southern taiga begins in earnest. Small herds merge with larger bands and these with still larger herds. In another week the separate bands are all bunched together in one enormous herd, perhaps two to three miles wide and ten to fifteen miles long. To be a witness to one of these mass migrations of caribou

moving across the Arctic tundra, southward, is a sight rare for human eyes.

Several summers ago I was lucky to see one of these spectacles in the Canadian Arctic. It occurred at a place some 500 miles northeast of Great Slave Lake, south of Bathurst Inlet. I was with Bob Ruttan, a Canadian wildlife biologist, who in turn was assisted by Archie Mendenville, a part Indian helper, and a small band of Eskimo workers employed as a caribou-tagging crew.

On our ninth day at Lake Contwoyto, apprehension began rising at our tagging camp, for no caribou were seen up to this point. But when our charter plane arrived from Yellowknife, Bob and the pilot and I took off immediately on a recon trip toward Mara Lake which, according to Bob, was our "last hope." We had flown several miles when Bob pointed his finger downward.

"Aw, go on," pilot Clem Bekar shouted back. "I looked that rockpile over when we passed it. They're rocks."

But Bob was right. They were caribou—thousands of them. We circled and came down low over them, snapping pictures as waves of stampeding hooves burst across the tundra. We repeated our 500-foot maneuver several times, then Bob selected a lake in their path and we headed down for a landing. The object was to quietly intercept the caribou on foot, get more photos, and do some censusing.

The maneuver worked perfectly. We landed and Bob and I took off across the country, heads low. Clem went to anchor our float plane and planned to join us later. The herd was coming in our direction all right, we could hear them, but no animals showed yet on the skyline. Still we could hear a massive rumbling in the distance, like thunder. My heart began pounding furiously in my chest. Then the first of several big bulls appeared on the skyline a quarter mile away. They carried enormous rocking-chair-like antlers and when joined soon by others, gave the appearance of moving trees. More appeared and still more—bulls and cows and young. We hugged the ground, seeking the protection of large boulders, and presently in the shadows of some large rocks, we set up our stations. Clem soon joined Bob at his post. I took to a lone rock.

The caribou began forming a semi-circle around us, and for the first time we could hear the clicking of their feet, a characteristic snapping of the bone joints and of their big flexible hooves. And out of the rumbling and thunder of their passage we began to detect the pig-like "grunk-grunk" of the cows and the similar but higher-pitched voices of the calves. Soon caribou were all around us, moving, snorting, clicking in an ever-increasing horde. In a few minutes, thousands of animals were crowded all around us, a bewildering mass of moving animaldom such as few persons have ever seen. Now thousands headed straight for us—now a hundred yards away, now fifty, now finally twenty—and then split as they detected us. We remained as motionless as marmots but I kept taking pictures and Bob counting: bulls, dry cows, cows with young, yearlings, separate calves. My heart pounded sharp drumbeats in my chest and neck as my whole being thrilled to the great wild spectacle.

On they came, in wave after wave, some passing as close as ten yards, others halting, growing suspicious after a long, hard look, then suddenly bolting. Now and then an alert bull sensed something strange, halted and dropped his head. And at twenty feet not liking what he saw or smelled, stretched out his right rear leg to full length, then suddenly sprang off in a loping gallop, stampeding hundreds, thousands of other animals. The roar from such a mass flight sounded like the waters of Niagara turned loose all at once.

For a full two hours the herd flowed past us. At times it seemed as if the whole tundra was a moving sea of caribou. Yet this was only the advance corps of 85,000 animals of the Bathurst herd. As it turned out, an even larger herd was passing around the other side of Mara Lake at that very moment and this herd amounted to another 115,000 animals. The grand total of the herd must have numbered 200,000 animals.

When the last of the caribou finally passed us, the sun was falling fast and we had to get out of the country. A breeze had picked up and Clem grew worried. He decided to take off alone and land again on a larger lake where take-off for the three of us would be easier. The plan worked.

At camp, it was soon, all *tuktu amihut,* which means "many caribou" in Eskimo. Excitement mounted, and for four days thereafter, it was all caribou talk: were they heading our way, when would they reach us, would they cross at the inlets expected, was everything ready for banding operation?

A week later all questions were answered. The caribou came, although at points further north than expected. Then a crowning blow fell. A freezing and fly-destroying north-west wind sprang up and blew constantly for several days. The entire herd, excepting for a few relatively small groups, turned into it and moved steadily away from the best tagging sites, to pass around the far end of Contwoyto Lake before swinging southward onto their old route to treeline. However, even then the alert and ever-watchful team of Eskimo hunters and Bob and Archie were able to catch and tag more than 300 animals.

The techniques for tagging caribou are simple enough, although not without danger to the taggers. Each animal is caught while attempting to swim an inlet or lake crossing and brought to the gunwale of the tagging boat, using a long-handled shepherd's crook, and then banded in the ear with a metal tag to which is attached a short, red fluorescent vinyl streamer. The animal is sexed, aged and then released. Tagged animals can thus be seen clearer and spotted easier from the air or when taken during the fall hunting season in the tree country where the caribou spread out. By recovering tags from the animals, biologists can find out how far the animals migrate, where they go, and much other useful information and data basic to good caribou management.

Several valuable facts are now coming to light through these investigations. Tagging has revealed, for example, that at least three large and fairly distinct herds occupy the Arctic mainland between Hudson's Bay (Baker Lake to Churchill) and the Mackenzie Valley. And although these herds do overlap and mix on their winter range, they "home" to their own summer ranges where they can be counted and thence managed according to the needs of the herd and the Eskimos of the area. Previous to tagging, investigators tended to underestimate actual numbers because of fear of duplication in counts where the herds were mixed. Also, it is now known for certain that there are more caribou than once was estimated. In fact, present numbers are now reaching a dangerously high level. These investigations also tend to show that sound biological facts and intelligent population management measures based upon scientific ecological facts, plus the maintenance of the natural but fragile habitat, are essential to keeping the barrenground caribou in a healthy relationship to food supplies, for the present and in the future.

The caribou year closes with most of the animals safe once again in the taiga, spread out once more across the great green coniferous forests, there to mate anew and await the onslaught of the long winter. Once again the elements take over, the sub-Arctic snows and the biting wind, followed by the purple cold of the Arctic itself.

Once more the Northland, the "land beyond the north wind," takes full command, for this is the natural cycle, the swing of the seasons, the Almanac of the Arctic world—a new land stronghold where, in the final analysis, all spells nature and everything that's living and all that's non-living must somehow be bent to its ways.

OUR WORLD
IN A NEW PERSPECTIVE

A Need for a Geobiotic Ethic

IN THE PRECEDING CHAPTERS I HAVE TRIED TO SHOW THAT WE LIVE IN AND are a part of a world of nature. It is a beautiful world, in many places rugged and fierce and wild, yet at times benign and tranquil and always changing. It is a good world and really the only one we know much about.

What seems disturbing these days are the great events which are shaping around us, in science and technology, in accelerated learning and accumulated knowledge, and yet how little our concern focuses on how to live. To my way of viewing things I must concede that I like whisper jets and hemlock glens, and I am willing to settle for a little of both, but not for jets alone. To those who would disagree, one can only say that any society that is willing to settle only for an artificial world is fleeing headlong toward a new kind of twenty-first century barbarism. When the swamp is gone and no birds sing and all is lifeless material, what will the spirit and character of man become?

Events in science and technology have come about with such swiftness, have struck with such force, that even the most skeptical of men now admit that "change" is a major characteristic of our time. Now that the race for outer space is on, one can only look with awe as the new science of astronautics gives us a glimpse of the exciting worlds to come. But what about our space on earth and the quality of its life? To see ourselves properly today, it seems to me, we should put ourselves in a clearer perspective in relation to time and space and nature.

About a million years ago on some distant mountainside, a shaggy two-legged creature squinted into the sun, blinked and wondered, "Who am I?" At this moment of time the creature became man, and becoming man commenced a long struggle to learn the meaning of life and man's place upon the earth. When this moment came, when man began to think, he left the animals behind and began a slow, tortuous climb toward a higher form of development.

What the early man thought of the earth, we do not know. Written history has come to us only in comparatively recent years. We did not know, for example, how to divide the year until the Egyptians worked out the calendar in 3,000 B.C. Ancient astronomers thought the earth was the center of the universe and it took Copernicus—approximately 2,000 years later—to reveal to the world that the earth was not the center of the universe but a planet that revolved around the sun. Yet it has been a mere hundred years since man first began to peer, significantly, into outer space.

For a long time we were led to believe that man's tenure on earth was a mere several thousand years. Then early geologists and paleontologists began talking about 50,000 and 100,000 years. Today the educated guess is that man has lived on earth at least a million years.

Similar is the story of the age of the earth. Not long ago the earth was said to be one billion years old. Now its age is placed at five or six billion years. Some scientists even claim the age of the earth as twelve billion years.

And what about present-day thinking about our solar system? Until man invented the telescope he could count perhaps 5,000 stars with the naked eye. With the coming of the small telescope, he soon found that there were at least 2,000,000 other stars! Now with the 200-inch Palomar in California he can see light from billions of stars!

Today astronomers tell us that the limit of human vision through the telescope is two billion light years. And a light year, we must be reminded, is the distance light travels in one year at the speed of 186,000 miles per second, or, some 6,000,000,000,000 miles. Our sun, the nearest star is 93,000,000 miles away, but *Alpha Centauri,* the nearest star other than the sun, is 4.4 light years away.

Five thousand years ago, a mere flash of time in the age of our universe, the night watchers over the Tigris and Euphrates rivers noticed bright, "wandering" stars in the heavens and wondered if they were different worlds. Today we know that these worlds are not stars but planets and are circling the sun much as our own planet does. Now we know that our solar system includes not only nine planets but 31 moons, 30,000 minor planets, and an uncountable number of meteors. What's more, our solar system in the Milky Way is but a speck in a much larger universe with hundreds, thousands, millions, perhaps billions of other galaxies, all stretching out into the dim recesses of time. Today astronomers peer into the awesome space of an endless universe some 2,000,000,000 light years away, or 12,000,000,000,000,000,000,000 miles as we know them! Beyond this lies only the vastness of the unknown where all physical laws of science and mathematics break down.

Worlds without end is what we see today. One afternoon our world is the Earth; the next morning it includes the great Sun. Then, perhaps on the evening of the second day, it shows as a universe with a galaxy of 100,000 million suns, " like sand . . . flung down by handfuls on the beach." Today, tonight we see our own galaxy as one among billions, perhaps trillions of other galaxies moving in space, where earth and satellites and suns and stars are ceaselessly being born, maturing and being snuffed out . . . in an incomprehensible universe of origin and time and space that has no beginning and no end.

It is estimated that during our remaining century we will spend in this country alone, many billions of dollars on research and development in outer space. Just how much money and how great an effort will be put into this program, no one can predict. But it is a fair guess that the amount will be more in dollars and human energy than any person can comprehend.

In recent years I have been attending a series of lecture-forums on research and development where the great problems of astronautical space are being discusssed and reviewed. One of the first major technological problems to be overcome in space travel, we are told, is the proper design and character of the space vehicles themselves, including the best types of propellants to use as ships move away from the gravitational pull of the earth. Travel in the intergalactic space region—a region many trillion miles away and where all sense of reality crumbles into only a vast unknown darkness—will not be easy.

To reach even the fringes of this vast region, perhaps around and beyond the great Milky Way, it will require space ships of an unheard of character. These alone will cost billions. According to a remarkable astronautical chart released by a scientific corporation, a space vehicle leaving the earth for outer space would encounter a number of travel zones in its path: first, the lower and upper atmospheres of the earth, with alternate zones of terrible cold and heat; then the area of terrestrial space, which is the area immediately above the earth's atmosphere. Then comes the cislunar and translunar spaces, with distances ranging from 10^4 to 10^5, or roughly 100,000 to 1,000,000 miles. Beyond this ring begins the interplanetary space, the region of the planets; further away still is the awesome interstellar space region, where the stars number into the trillions and only time has meaning. Finally, beyond all these regions, there unfolds the most remote space region of all—the intergalactic space where only light-years count and mathematical calculations fall apart and lose meaning.

For man to travel to and from even the lower space regions nearest the earth, some scientists warn, will take some doing. First to be licked are the vast technological problems that surround lifting a sizable man-made object into distant space. They warn further that the long and involved countdown in our rocket firing must be reduced.

But many of our technical problems can be overcome, given sufficient time and money and brain power. What worries astronauts and some biologists is not the technological know-how, but the incomprehensible human and psychological and biological problems that man must overcome to live in space. Such things as weightlessness, which often causes nausea and delirium and such problems as long-period food supply and the reproduction of new generations of human species while in space, are only a few of the complex space-adjustment problems that will have to be solved—and these are among our most difficult to solve even on earth. Such things as food problems where human wastes may be linked to algae in a perpetual food chain and social arrangements as intermarriage with closely confined space groups may have distasteful psychological barriers which may not be easily overcome.

Thus I share the anxiety of many biologists and sociologists who believe that these intensely complex human barriers may be among our most difficult problems to solve and man's effort at their resolution may lead to his Armageddon. The question posed is: Was man meant to go exploring through distant outer space? One only has to look at our immediate space problems on earth—the earth we know reasonably well—to realize that we haven't done such a superb job of ironing out our natural and human problems here to go on probing too far and too deep into distant pastures.

It seems to me as a biologist that unless men of leadership and wisdom recognize the growing importance of natural space on earth and its related problems, our race to the moon and other satellites will be of little avail. Today America faces some of the most serious domestic crises in its history. The problems of skyrocketing population, control of people, urbanization, education, and the swallowing up of vast chunks of our natural countryside, all pose as major dilemmas that need solving.

Take the problem of open space. Year by year, month by month, day by day, the engulfment of woods and wet areas and beach country continues. Each hour the siphoning tentacles of encroachment draw away at the vitals of our forests, meadows, marshes, swamps, scenic areas, and homes of wildlife—*natural* areas all and all with great existing or potential recreational, economic, biological and esthetic value. Each year we lose over one million acres of land to urban development, subdivisions, highways, shopping centers, industrial plants. In all great metropolitan centers, cities are losing their natural "wild" places as one urban agglomeration after another merges with development centers, often "slurbs" of the next. Natural spots of hinterland, scenic water areas, picturesque hills and dales, haunting wild beaches are swiftly vanishing. More and more, families must travel greater distances to find a bit of shade or a place of solitude. More and more the outdoorsman must drive longer to find a place to pitch a tent or wet a fishing line.

Nothing is more disheartening to the modern naturalist these days than to see parcel after parcel of natural space sacrificed completely in a passion for urban "growth and development," to see so little regard for open space, green areas, and wild things and places.

In my work I have a good opportunity to see what is happening to America, the land our forefathers fought so hard to establish and to pass on to us with the solemn admonition: *take care of this land lest you sell our heritage down the river.* Having recently covered over one million miles of the continent by air, rail, automobile, horseback, boat, and afoot, I am appalled by what I see.

For example, here I see one metropolitan area—some 300,000 in population—growing like wildfire. But a closer look shows that little is being done to provide additional public parks, parkways and recreation areas, and there's little concern to save disappearing surrounding scenic areas. Juvenile crime is increasing, yet nothing is being done to provide wholesome recreation for young people. Instead, one is told: "What this city needs is more industry."

Of course our nation needs houses and supermarkets and highways. We need to keep our economy going. Yet the rational man must ask: Is it necessary to sacrifice *everything* for the sake of development, for the sake of so-called *growth?* What about the quality of our environment and life on earth?

Let's cite another example. Here is a piece of land near a small city, 72 acres to be exact. It is going down before the bulldozers. It was lovely woodland and farm country hinterland since Plymouth Rock. Its trees and ladyslippers and small creatures were wild for eons of time. Now it is going. When the white man came to replace the Indian, he cleared some of the land but he saved some of these woods, kept a small marsh intact for muskrats and wood ducks. He let the ladyslippers grow. Fine land it was, rolling, airy, beautiful. It would have made a picturesque park someday, for the city residents and its suburbanites. But no. Economics decreed that it be sold for $2,000 an acre and turned into home development. So the bulldozers are tearing out the trees, leveling the hillocks, scooping out the last spring and meadow. Not one pine will be left. Not one root of hepatica will remain under the cool blanket of leaves when the developers get through.

The town will lose (and already has lost) its last remaining site for a small park.

The United States proper has a land surface area of 2,973,700 square miles. Three hundred years ago most of this area was wild land, with great stands of oaks, pines, hemlocks, sparkling watercourses and woods, prairies and grasslands untouched by man.

Today the wild country has shrunk to approximately two and two-tenths percent of the total land area. The country's remaining wilderness lands would fit into an area the size of Georgia. They may shrink still more.

America's wild land is important. For the immigrant who arrived yesterday and for the fourth generation "American," it is a symbol of the nation. It represents a pioneer heritage in which the individual, not the machine, is valued.

Every 12 seconds our population increases by one person. Each year there are increasing demands on our natural resources. More persons seek recreation; greater demands are made on water, wildlife, the green landscape, and minerals. In the face of our increasing population and the growing mechanization of so much of our land and life, our main hope for retaining some aspect of a natural environment in our midst lies in a policy of deliberate preservation, wise zoning, effective planning, good management, and controlled human use.

What is needed everywhere in America is an immediate and long-range program of action to save what remains of our open space and wild lands, to save what public lands we still possess, to acquire new public lands wherever they can be found, and to set aside family-size parks and community educational nature centers outside every community in America.

Unless we are deliberate in our efforts to save some of our natural environment on earth and make man responsible to it, our race to the lifeless moon and the stars will be of little use. If man cannot make a good home on the planet Earth, a place that has sustained life so well for so many eons, then attempting to settle a bleak no-man's-land in outer space seems foolish indeed.

Fortunately there are signs that man is beginning to learn that he cannot live by bread and gadgets alone. His body may yearn for satisfaction of certain biological needs and comforts and, when these are satisfied momentarily and the mind is free for the reasoning and creative process, there still remains something missing. There is still the eternal search for spiritual achievement, for "peace of soul." Man needs the esthetic in life to feed his being or he is soon dead. Man needs the beauty of lands and waters, to have his heart stirred by wild creatures, wild places. He needs the refreshment and exhilaration of fresh air in his lungs, the occasional clear vision of unspoiled wilderness before him. All these fulfill a deeper need, answer an ancient hunger for inner peace. Man's need for a sense of balance and order and for things in their proper places in the environment is one of the strongest reasons for conservation. For when all that is man is gone, what else? Then, as the poet said, Nature alone is permanent; Nature *remains.*

Conservation, then, in modern times, demands something more than men. Our efforts today require more than money. They demand an appreciation by people for intangibles, a feeling of respect and reverence toward the earth and all that dwells upon it. The late Aldo Leopold had this in mind when he talked about a land ethic, an ecological conscience. Dr. Albert Schweitzer spoke of it in his philosophy of reverence for life, love for all living things. And Joseph Wood Krutch made the observation that without sentiment conservation alone is not enough.

And what about the long-range physical and mental health values of the outdoors? Within a few short generations we have changed our way of life appreciably. Our forebears largely used their hands and muscles to make a living. Today most people earn a living with their brains, using machines and pushbuttons and swivel chairs, only to come home to a night of passive entertainment and physical inactivity. Little wonder the American people are consuming, according to a Congressional subcommittee report, some $280,000,000 worth of tranquilizers each year. And despite medical science, these appalling changes in our way of life, together with the growing tensions of complicated living, are taking a frightful toll of human life. According to one reliable medical report, coronary heart disease is the number one killer in the United States. The disease rate is highest in the western world and here the United States is in the lead. Moreover, the disease was highest in New York State and, not surprising, highest in New York City as compared with the rest of the nation. Nearly 3,000 persons die of the disease each day in the United States alone.

A study of the physical fitness of our youth, compared to the youth of southern Europe, reveals an impressive result. American youth failed 78.3 percent of the tests; the Europeans failed only 8.3 percent.

The central point being made by these references is that the world of nature, and all that it holds, has values in physical and mental refreshment which can do much for mankind. If we lose our strongly conditioning environment, either in quantity or quality, we will be that much weaker for it. Today we need the ultimate in physical and mental health if our progress toward a better life is to be realized.

To talk of an ethic may appear to some as useless sentimentality. But the question arises, "Is sentiment as powerless as it may seem to guide a people toward a nobler purpose?" How great can any man, any nation, become if all is measured by the dollar sign and things material?

There exists within us, one supposes, a fundamental purpose in being, a sense of gratitude and ways of showing it. We, in America, have been generous in our regard for the great men of the past who have helped build our nation. Yet we must remember that much of their greatness was due to the natural lavishness of a great land. The early Greeks worshipped their gods who gave them land and beauty and grain. Is it less wise for us, in our age, to ask that we commemorate to generous safekeeping a portion of the natural world to those yet unborn? This seems a question of ethics, a matter of fundamental correctness and national decency. How are we to shape our future if we do not leave for ourselves and our children some examples—and some scientific samples—of some of our natural heritage?

There is a distinct need then, it seems to me, for the emergence of a strong ecological consciousness among men, a sensitivity and a sentimentality toward the Good Earth which sustains us—a feeling of reverence and respect toward all the inanimate things of the earth and all the living things that dwell upon it. For want of a better term, such a feeling or attitude might be called a geobiotic ethic.

We do not have such an ethic today. Such an ethic, such a conscience, needs to be created. To create it we need more knowledge, better training, improved outdoor interpretation. Above all, we need a major focus on nature appreciation in our education, on ecology and on the role of man in the natural world.

Perhaps the genius which helped to transform America into the most industrialized, into the most technological nation on earth, now can be turned toward another equally important task—the task of ennobling the human personality with a more benevolent man and nature understanding and relationship. Viewing our world in natural systems, a series of large and small interlocked worlds with man as a key entity, as I've tried to reveal in this book, is one promising approach.

RECOMMENDED READING

Bates, Marston. *Forests and the Sea*. New York: Random House. 1960.

Buchsbaum, Ralph and Mildred. *Basic Ecology*. Pittsburgh, Pa.: The Boxwood Press. 1964.

Carson, Rachel. *The Edge of the Sea*. Boston: Houghton Mifflin Co. 1955.

Costello, David F. *The Prairie World*. New York: Thomas Y. Crowell Co. 1969.

Darling, Frank Fraser. *Wilderness and Plenty*. New York: A Friends of the Earth/Ballantine Book. 1970.

Farb, Peter. *Face of North America*. New York: Harper and Row, Publishers. 1963.

Grossman, Louise and Shelley and John N. Hamlet. *Our Vanishing Wilderness*. New York: Grossett and Dunlap, Publishers. 1969.

Hamilton, Michael. *This Little Planet*. New York: Charles Scribner's Sons. 1970.

Krutch, Joseph Wood. *The Twelve Seasons*. New York: William Sloane Associates. 1967.

Leopold, Aldo. *Sand County Almanac*. New York: Oxford University Press. 1949.

Meadows, Donnella H., Dennis L. Meadows, Jorgen Randers, and William W. Behrens III. *The Limits to Growth*. New York: Universe Books. 1972.

Rienow, Robert and Leona Train Rienow. *Moment in the Sun*. New York: Ballantine Books. 1970.

Saltonstall, Richard, Jr. *Your Environment and What You Can Do About It*. New York: Walker & Co. 1970.

Sears, Paul B. *The Living Landscape*. New York: Basic Books, Inc. 1966.

Shomon, Joseph J. *Open Land for Urban America*. Baltimore, Md.: The Johns Hopkins Press. 1972.